Key Stage 3 Maths is a complete revision and classroom companion. It comprises clear, concise content, covering everything in the programme of study for this key stage, plus tasks and questions to reinforce learning and help improve confidence. As such, it provides a user-friendly and cost-effective alternative to traditional revision guides with separate workbooks.

This book is intended for pupils who will be sitting the Tier 5-8 papers in the National Curriculum Mathematics Tests at the end of Year 9. It can also be used for extension work by pupils sitting the Tier 3-6 papers. It is meticulously matched to the programme of study for Key Stage 3 and the material is organised into different levels, according to the attainment targets set out in the National Curriculum.

For ease of use, the pages are colour-coded according to level. Material for **Levels 5 and 6** can be found on the **blue** pages. Material for **Levels 7 and 8** can be found on the **green** pages.

As it is aimed at the higher tier, this book assumes that pupils already have a good grasp of the skills and concepts covered at Levels 3 and 4. Throughout the book **'You should already know...'** headings signpost ideas that pupils should already be familiar with. This material is covered in greater detail in Key Stage 3 Maths: Levels 3-6 Revision and Classroom Companion.

The book is arranged into four sections: Number; Algebra; Shape, Space & Measure; and Handling Data. Each section is broken down into topics.

Within each topic, the Level 7 and 8 material follows on immediately from the Level 5 and 6 material to provide obvious progression. All pupils, regardless of ability, should revise the Level 5 and 6 pages as they provide an essential platform to the higher material.

Each page starts with bullet points identifying exactly what the pupil needs to know. It then provides clear explanations with easy-to-follow, worked examples, followed by questions for the pupil to complete, ensuring they can use the different skills to solve problems accurately.

Consultant Editor: John Proctor
An Education Consultant with over 13 years teaching experience, John Proctor is an expert in Mathematics and Computer Science. He is the former Director of Specialist College, St. Mary's Catholic High School in Astley.

Contributors:

Linda Bakes - has over 21 years experience teaching mathematics. She has also lectured in the subject at Leeds Metropolitan University and worked as a Mathematics Consultant to West Yorkshire Education Business Services.

Susan Ball - As a marker for National Curriculum Tests in Mathematics, Susan Ball knows better than most where pupils struggle and make mistakes. An experienced teacher and lecturer, she is already an established maths author with several Key Stage 3 text books and teacher's resources already in print.

...Browse for a full list of publications and further information

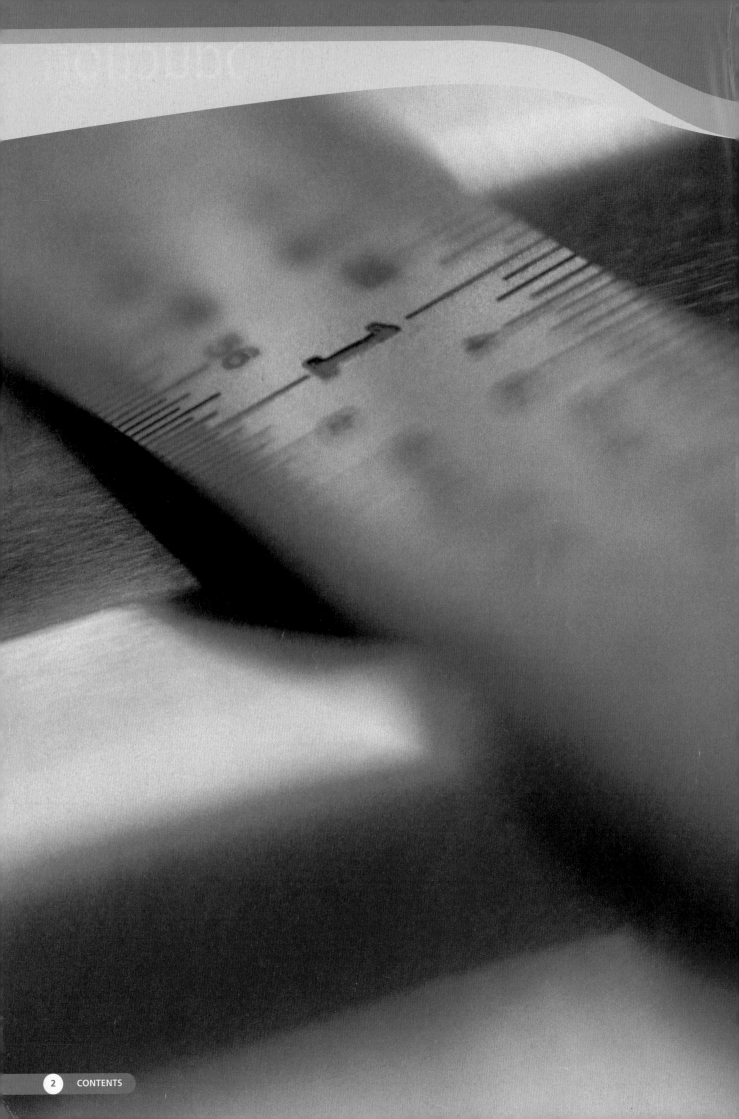

Contents

✓ You should already know...

- **that the digits in numbers have different place values**
- **that place value can help to put positive numbers in size order**
- **how to add and subtract positive numbers.**

ℹ You also need to know...

- **how to order positive and negative numbers**
- **how to add and subtract negative numbers in context.**

Look at the number line below:

smaller -5 -4 -3 -2 -1 0 1 2 3 4 5 bigger

Positive numbers are placed on the number line to the right of 0 (zero). The further to the **right** a number is, the **bigger** it is. Negative numbers are placed on the number line to the left of 0 (zero). The further to the **left** a number is, the **smaller** it is.

Positive and negative whole numbers are called **integers**. If you are given a selection of integers and asked to put them in order of size, you will find a number line very useful.

You can use the number line to add and subtract numbers too. To add, count up the scale. To subtract, count down the scale.

Examples

1 Put these numbers in ascending order (smallest first): 5, 8, -4, 0, -1, 7, 3, -3.

First, group all the negative numbers together on the left and the positive numbers on the right then put them in order.

-4, -3, -1, 0, 3, 5, 7, 8

2 On a winter morning, the temperature is -3°C. By lunchtime the temperature has risen to 5°C. What is this change in temperature in °C?

Find the starting temperature (-3°C). Now count up the scale to the finishing temperature (5°C).

Change in temperature = +8°C

> You were counting up the scale, so the answer is positive. If you had been counting down the scale, the answer would have been negative.

? Now try these...

1 Put these numbers in descending order (biggest first):
-7, 8, 3, -6, 1, 9, 2

2 Put these numbers in ascending order (smallest first):
5, -9, -2, 0, 3, -7, 6

3 Put these numbers in ascending order (smallest first). You might have to extend the number line or draw a new one to help you.
11, -16, 25, 4, -7, 6, 0, -8, -15, 12

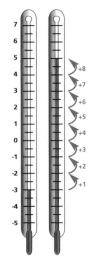

4 Look at this thermometer. It reads 9°C.
a) If the temperature rises by 2°C what will the thermometer read?
b) If it then falls by 15°C what will it read?
c) By how many °C will it have to rise to get back to 9°C?

Integers

ℹ You need to know...

- **how to add and subtract negative numbers.**

You also need to be able to add and subtract negative numbers without relying on a number line.

When an addition or subtraction involves negative numbers, look at all the signs in the calculation. Positive numbers don't have a + sign written in front of them, but they must still be taken into account.

When **two signs appear side by side**, e.g. 7 + (-6) =, the following rule tells you whether to add or subtract the second number:

If the signs are the **same** this means **add**.

$$+ \quad + \quad + \quad = \quad +$$

$$- \quad + \quad - \quad = \quad +$$

If the signs are **different** it means **subtract**.

$$+ \quad + \quad - \quad = \quad -$$

$$- \quad + \quad + \quad = \quad -$$

You can then perform the calculation.

Examples

Work out the following...

1 a) 5 + 7 =
5 + (+7) = | + + + = + |
5 + 7 = 12

b) -5 + 7 =
-5 + (+7) = | + + + = + |
-5 + 7 = 2

c) 5 – 7 =
5 – (+7) = | – + + = – |
5 – 7 = -2

d) -5 – 7 =
-5 – (+7) = | – + + = – |
-5 – 7 = -12

2 a) 5 + (-7) = | + + – = – |
5 – 7 = -2

b) -5 + (-7) = | + + – = – |
-5 – 7 = -12

c) 5 – (-7) = | – + – = + |
5 + 7 = 12

d) -5 – (-7) = | – + – = + |
-5 + 7 = 2

❓ Now try these...

1. 11 + 6
2. -6 + 9
3. 5 – 17
4. -9 + 6
5. -4 – 8
6. 5 + (-6)
7. -8 – (+2)
8. 0 – (-10)
9. -14 – (-6)
10. 15 + (-15)
11. 12 – (-7)
12. -4 + 16
13. -17 + (-3)
14. 0 + (-13)
15. 2 + 7
16. -7 – (-14)
17. 6 + 15
18. 5 – 8
19. 12 – 9
20. -3 – (-18)

Multiplication and Division

✓ You should already know...

- the multiplication tables up to 10 x 10
- how to multiply and divide by 10, 100 or 1000
- that multiplication and division are inverse operations
- how to use written methods of short multiplication and division
- how to solve whole number problems involving multiplication and division, including those giving rise to remainders.

ⓘ You also need to know...

- how to use an appropriate non-calculator method for multiplying and dividing large numbers
- how to multiply and divide negative numbers.

To multiply large numbers, you need to use a method called **long multiplication**.

As shown in Example 1, perform separate multiplications for each digit in the multiplier and then add your results together. Write down your working at each stage so you don't lose track!

Long division works in the same way as short division. However, because you are working with large numbers, keep track of your carrying underneath to avoid confusion.

To multiply and divide positive and negative numbers, ignore the signs and calculate as normal. The following rules determine whether the answer is positive or negative:

If the signs are the **same**, the answer is **positive**

$$+ \times + = + \qquad + \div + = +$$
$$- \times - = + \qquad - \div - = +$$

If the signs are **different**, the answer is **negative**

$$+ \times - = - \qquad + \div - = -$$
$$- \times + = - \qquad - \div + = -$$

Examples

1

$$
\begin{array}{r}
3\,6\,1 \\
\times \quad 5\,4 \\
\hline
1\,8^30\,5\,0 \\
+\ 1\,4^24\,4 \\
\hline
1\,9\,4\,9\,4
\end{array}
$$

> 54 is **50** + **4** so we start by multiplying **361** by **50** and then by **4** separately

> Start with **361 x 50** – Put a **0** in the Units column and then do **361 x 5. 5 x 1 = 5** write down **5**. **5 x 6 = 30** write down **0** and carry the **3** along. **5 x 3 = 15** then add the **3** to give **18**. Write down **18**.

> Now start again to find **361 x 4**. **4 x 1 = 4** write down **4**. **4 x 6 = 24** write down **4** and carry the **2** along. **4 x 3 = 12** then add the **2** to give **14**. Write down **14**.

> Now add the two answers together (ignore any previous 'carry' numbers!)

2

$$
\begin{array}{r}
0\,3\,8 \\
14\,\overline{)\,5\,3\,2} \\
4\,2\,\downarrow \\
\hline
1\,1\,2 \\
1\,1\,2 \\
\hline
0
\end{array}
$$

> **14** does not divide into **5** so move on.

> **14** into **53** goes **3** times. **14 x 3 = 42**. Write **42** below the **53** and subtract to give **11**.

> Bring down the **2**. **14** into **112** goes **8** times. **14 x 8 = 112**. Write this below and subtract to give **0**. This means there is no remainder.

> Use the same layouts as examples 1 and 2 then look at the rules on the left to work out the signs

3 $361 \times -54 = -19\,494$

4 $-532 \div -14 = 38$

? Now try these...

1
$$
\begin{array}{r}
5\,4\,9 \\
\times \quad 1\,5 \\
\hline
\end{array}
$$

2
$$
\begin{array}{r}
7\,0\,4 \\
\times \quad 2\,8 \\
\hline
\end{array}
$$

3
$$
\begin{array}{r}
-3\,5\,6 \\
\times \quad 2\,9 \\
\hline
\end{array}
$$

5 $18\,\overline{)\,4\,3\,2}$

6 $23\,\overline{)\,3\,9\,1}$

7 $-56\,\overline{)\,2\,2\,4}$

8 $-42\,\overline{)\,-8\,8\,2}$

Powers and Roots

✓ You should already know...

- that a power shows a number is to be multiplied by itself and by how many times
- that a number to the power of 2 is squared
- that a number to the power of 3 is cubed

ⓘ You also need to know...

- what a square root is
- what a cube root is.

As with any multiplication, when you square or cube a number the result is called the product.

The reverse of squaring a number is to **square root**. This will take you from the product back to the original number. You should learn the square roots of the first few square numbers.

$2^2 = 4$ $\sqrt{4} = 2$	$3^2 = 9$ $\sqrt{9} = 3$	$4^2 = 16$ $\sqrt{16} = 4$
$5^2 = 25$ $\sqrt{25} = 5$	$6^2 = 36$ $\sqrt{36} = 6$	$7^2 = 49$ $\sqrt{49} = 7$
$8^2 = 64$ $\sqrt{64} = 8$	$9^2 = 81$ $\sqrt{81} = 9$	$10^2 = 100$ $\sqrt{100} = 10$

Remember...
$2^2 = 2 \times 2$
$2^3 = 2 \times 2 \times 2$

The reverse of cubing a number is to **cube root**.

Most calculators should have ☑ and ☒ for finding the square root and cube root of a number. Make sure you know how to use yours. Cube root is sometimes written as $x^{\frac{1}{3}}$.

Examples

This is the square root symbol

① $\quad 7^2 = \quad 49 \quad$ so $\quad \sqrt{49} = \quad 7$
② $\quad 15^2 = 225 \quad$ so $\quad \sqrt{225} = 15$
③ $\quad 4^3 = \quad 64 \quad$ so $\quad \sqrt[3]{64} = \quad 4$
④ $\quad 7^3 = 343 \quad$ so $\quad \sqrt[3]{343} = \quad 7$

This is the cube root symbol

❓ Now try these...

Use a calculator to find...

1. $\sqrt{289}$
2. $\sqrt{225}$
3. $\sqrt{400}$
4. $\sqrt{169}$
5. $\sqrt{324}$
6. $\sqrt{625}$
7. $\sqrt[3]{343}$
8. $\sqrt[3]{729}$
9. $\sqrt[3]{2744}$

Without using a calculator, find the following square roots:

10. $\sqrt{36}$
11. $\sqrt{100}$
12. $\sqrt{81}$

✓ You should already know...

- that even numbers divide by 2 exactly
- that odd numbers cannot be divided exactly by 2
- that factors are the numbers which divide exactly into a given number
- that multiples are numbers produced by multiplying a given number.

i You also need to know...

- **how to identify prime numbers.**

A **prime number** is a number that has exactly two factors – itself and 1. It is worth trying to memorise all the prime numbers under 100 (see below).

1 is not classed as a prime number. It is unique in that it only has one factor and that is 1. **2** is the only even prime number.

Example

Put a circle around all the prime numbers in this number grid.

1	②	③	4	⑤	6	⑦	8	9	10
⑪	12	⑬	14	15	16	⑰	18	⑲	20
21	22	㉓	24	25	26	27	28	㉙	30
㉛	32	33	34	35	36	㊲	38	39	40
㊶	42	㊸	44	45	46	㊼	48	49	50
51	52	(53)	54	55	56	57	58	(59)	60
(61)	62	63	64	65	66	(67)	68	69	70
(71)	72	(73)	74	75	76	77	78	(79)	80
81	82	(83)	84	85	86	87	88	(89)	90
91	92	93	94	95	96	(97)	98	99	100

If you know your multiplication tables you will be able to eliminate all the numbers that are NOT prime numbers easily.

If you suspect a number might be prime, try dividing it by 2, 3, 5, 7, 9 etc. If you can divide it exactly – it's not a prime number!

? Now try these...

1. Which of these numbers are prime numbers? (try to answer this question without looking at the chart on this page!)
   11, 33, 23, 73, 91, 39, 101

2. State whether the following are prime numbers and explain your answer:
   a) 94
   b) 29

Types of Number

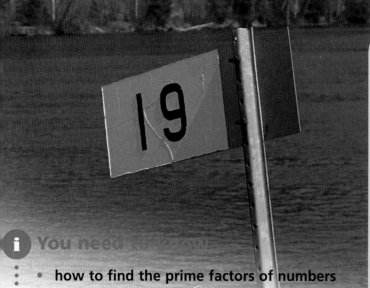

i You need to know...

- **how to find the prime factors of numbers**
- **how to find the highest common factor and least common multiple of two or more numbers.**

All numbers can be written as a product of **prime factors**. These are simply factors that are also prime numbers. To calculate all the prime factors of a number, divide repeatedly by prime numbers.

The **highest common factor** of two (or more) numbers is the highest factor that divides exactly into both (or all) of the numbers. To find the highest common factor, write down all the factors of each number in prime factor form. Find all the factors that appear in both lists. Multiplying these numbers together gives the highest common factor.

The **least common multiple** of two (or more) numbers is the lowest number that is a multiple of both (or all) of the numbers. To find the least common multiple, write down the first ten multiples of each number, then compare the lists to find the numbers that appear on both lists. The smallest of these is the least common multiple.

Examples

1 Find the prime factors of 180.
Work with one prime number at a time.
Upside down division layout is best:

2	180	Start with 2, then again...
2	90	
3	45	2 won't divide exactly into 45, so try 3...
3	15	And again, then use 5...
5	5	
	1	You've finished when you get to 1

So the prime factors of **180** are **2, 3** and **5**.
This can also be written as
2 x 2 x 3 x 3 x 5 or **2² x 3² x 5**.

2 Express 1020 as a product of prime factors.

2	1020	
2	510	
5	255	It doesn't matter that we used 5 before 3
3	51	
17	17	
	1	

So **1020 = 2 x 2 x 3 x 5 x 17**
or **2² x 3 x 5 x 17**

3 Find the highest common factor of 72 and 80.

Write all the prime factors of both numbers... and then circle the common factors.

72 = ⎡2 x 2 x 2⎤ x 3 x 3
80 = ⎣2 x 2 x 2⎦ x 2 x 5

Then multiply the common prime factors together to find the highest common factor.

2 x 2 x 2 = 8

4 Find the least common multiple of 5 and 8.

Write down the first ten multiples of each number...

5, 10, 15, 20, 25, 30, 35, (40), 45, 50
8, 16, 24, 32, (40), 48, 56, 64, 72, 80

Then look for the numbers that appear in both lists. The lowest of these numbers is your least common multiple.

= 40

? Now try these...

1 What are the prime factors of 108?

2 Express 1 500 as a product of prime factors.

3 What is the highest common factor of 210 and 108?

4 What is the least common multiple of 7 and 9?

i You need to know...

- **what a reciprocal is.**

The **reciprocal** of a number is one 'over' that number, i.e. 1 divided by that number. A reciprocal is therefore a fraction (see p.12-15).

The reciprocal of a fraction is simply that fraction turned upside down, for example, the reciprocal of $\frac{2}{3}$ is $\frac{3}{2}$. This is how you arrive at the reciprocal of a fraction...

Reciprocal of $\frac{2}{3} = \frac{1}{\frac{2}{3}} = 1 \times \frac{3}{2} = \frac{3}{2}$

Remember, when you divide by a fraction, you actually turn it upside down and then multiply it (see p.13).

You can also use your calculator to work out the decimal value of a reciprocal. To find the reciprocal of $\frac{3}{4}$ key in

$1 \div 3$ [a$\frac{b}{c}$] $4 =$ ⌐ 1⌐1⌐3 ⌐

Pressing the [a$\frac{b}{c}$] button again will convert the fraction into a decimal (**1.3333333 which means** $1\frac{1}{3}$ **or** $\frac{4}{3}$)

Reciprocals can also be written in the form **n^{-1}**. This means **1 ÷ n**.

Examples

Write the reciprocal of each number...

1 5   **The reciprocal of 5 is** $\frac{1}{5}$**.**

2 14   **The reciprocal of 14 is** $\frac{1}{14}$**.**

3 $\frac{1}{12}$ **The reciprocal of** $\frac{1}{12}$ **is 12.**

4 $\frac{2}{3}$ **The reciprocal of** $\frac{2}{3}$ **is** $\frac{3}{2}$**.**   Check it on your calculator

5 $\frac{4}{5}$ **The reciprocal of** $\frac{4}{5}$ **is** $\frac{5}{4}$**.**

? Now try these...

1 Write the reciprocal of each number...

a) 8   d) $\frac{2}{4}$ g) 0.5

b) 11   e) $\frac{6}{5}$ h) 0.25

c) $\frac{1}{3}$ f) $\frac{1}{65}$

2 Write the following as reciprocals...

a) 6^{-1}

b) 25^{-1}

c) 2^{-1}

d) 45^{-1}

Types of Number

ℹ️ You need to know...

- **how to solve problems involving numbers expressed in standard form.**

Standard form is a method of writing all numbers in a common format regardless of their size. This is especially useful for very, very large or very, very small numbers where lots of zeros might otherwise be needed to show the place value of the digits. Numbers written in standard form always look like this...

$$A \times 10^n$$

A is a number from 1 up to but not including 10 ($1 \leq A < 10$)

n is a whole number (or integer)

If the original number is greater than 1, the power of 10 will be a positive number. If it is less than 1 the power will be negative. The power of 10 (n) tells you in which direction and how many places to move the decimal point.

❓ Now try these...

1 Write these in standard form:
- **a)** 5500
- **b)** 675 000
- **c)** 1370 000 000
- **d)** 12 500
- **e)** 0.00012
- **f)** 0.06
- **g)** 0.5
- **h)** 0.00001

2 Write these as normal numbers:
- **a)** 5.1×10^4
- **b)** 6.725×10^2
- **c)** 1.21×10^{-4}
- **d)** 4.99×10^{-2}
- **e)** 1.4×10^7
- **f)** 9.9×10^1
- **g)** 5.63×10^{-5}
- **h)** 3.33×10^{-1}

Examples

Write the following numbers in standard form.

1 **594 000**

5.94

594000 (moving over 5 4 3 2 1 places)

$$= 5.94 \times 10^5$$

- Write down the digits before the zeros and insert a decimal point after the first digit.
- Look at the original number and count how many places the decimal point has been moved to get to the new number. This number becomes the power.
- A number greater than 1 has a positive power.

2 **2 000**

$$= 2 \times 10^3$$

3 **370 000 000**

$$= 3.7 \times 10^8$$

4 **0.000594**

5.94

0.000594 (moving over 1 2 3 4 places)

$$= 5.94 \times 10^{-4}$$

- Write down the digits after the zeros and insert a decimal point after the first digit.
- Look at the original number and count how many places the decimal point has been moved to get to the new number. This number becomes the power.
- A number less than 1 has a negative power.

5 **0.1256**

$$= 1.256 \times 10^{-1}$$

6 **0.0000045**

$$= 4.5 \times 10^{-6}$$

✓ You should already know...

- **that equivalent fractions are different fractions of equal value.**

ℹ You also need to know...

- **how to find equivalent fractions**
- **how to simplify fractions.**

Chains of equivalent fractions can be created by multiplying the numerator and denominator by the same number.

We know that multiplying is the mathematical opposite of dividing, so we can also create a chain of equivalent fractions by dividing the numerator and denominator by the same number. This is known as **simplifying** or **cancelling down**.

When a number consists of a whole number AND a fraction it can be written in two ways: as an **improper fraction** or as a **mixed number**.

? Now try these...

1. By multiplying by 3 each time, find four fractions equivalent to $\frac{2}{5}$.
2. Using any multiplier, find four fractions equivalent to $\frac{1}{7}$.
3. Divide by 2 each time to simplify $\frac{48}{64}$.
4. Describe the quantity represented by the blue areas of these diagrams as both a mixed number and an improper fraction.

   a)  b)

5. Convert $3\frac{1}{4}$ to an improper fraction.
6. Convert $\frac{17}{6}$ to a mixed number.
7. Convert $5\frac{1}{3}$ to an improper fraction.
8. Convert $\frac{32}{5}$ to a mixed number.
9. Convert $\frac{32}{12}$ to a mixed number and simplify the fraction.

Examples

1 Create a chain of equivalent fractions by multiplying the numerator and the denominator of $\frac{1}{2}$ by 3.

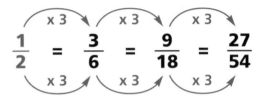

$$\frac{1}{2} = \frac{3}{6} = \frac{9}{18} = \frac{27}{54}$$

2 Create a chain of fractions by dividing the numerator and the denominator of $\frac{48}{64}$ by 4.

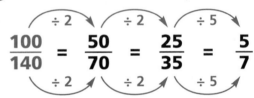

$$\frac{48}{64} = \frac{12}{16} = \frac{3}{4}$$

3 Simplify (or cancel down) $\frac{100}{140}$.

$$\frac{100}{140} = \frac{50}{70} = \frac{25}{35} = \frac{5}{7}$$

4 Look at the pizza.

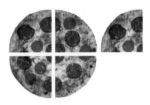

a) How many quarters of pizza are there altogether?

   There are 5 quarters of pizza.

b) Write this as a fraction.

   $\frac{5}{4}$. **This is an improper fraction.**

   > Improper fractions are 'top heavy.'
   > The numerator is larger than the denominator.

c) Write this as a mixed number.

   $1\frac{1}{4}$. **This tells us that there is one whole pizza and an extra quarter of pizza.**

Fractions

ℹ You need to know...

- **how to add and subtract fractions by writing them with a common denominator**
- **how to multiply and divide fractions.**

To add or subtract fractions, they *must* have the same denominator. If the fractions you are given don't have the same denominator, you will need to find equivalent fractions (see p.12) that do.

The numerators can then simply be added or subtracted. Sometimes the answer can be 'tidied up' by simplifying the fraction or changing an improper fraction to a mixed number.

Fractions can also be multiplied. All you do is multiply the numerators together, and then multiply the denominators together. Remember to simplify your answer.

To divide fractions there is a trick: turn the second fraction upside down and then multiply it with the first, as explained above.

You can use the $\boxed{a^b_c}$ button on a calculator to work with fractions. To work out $\frac{3}{4} - \frac{2}{5}$, press **3** $\boxed{a^b_c}$ **4 − 2** $\boxed{a^b_c}$ **5 =** It's as easy as that! To key in $1\frac{3}{5}$, press **1** $\boxed{a^b_c}$ **3** $\boxed{a^b_c}$ **5**. If your calculator has $\boxed{\frac{d}{c}}$ function you can use this to convert a mixed number into an improper fraction. Pressing $\boxed{a^b_c}$ again will convert the fraction into a decimal.

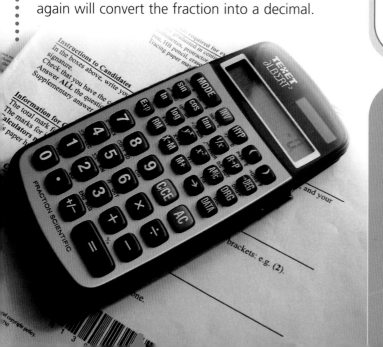

Examples

1 $\frac{1}{5} + \frac{2}{5} = \frac{3}{5}$

> Both the denominators are **5**, so the addition can be done straight away.

2 $\frac{3}{4} - \frac{2}{5}$

> **4** and **5** are both factors of **20** so use twentieths.

$\frac{15}{20} - \frac{8}{20} = \frac{7}{20}$

> Don't forget to multiply the numerator!

3 $\frac{3}{4} + \frac{5}{8}$

> **4** and **8** are both factors of **8** so use eighths.

$\frac{6}{8} + \frac{5}{8} = \frac{11}{8} = \mathbf{1}\frac{3}{8}$

> This is an improper fraction. $\frac{11}{8} = \mathbf{1}$ remainder **3**

4 $\frac{2}{5} \times \frac{3}{4} = \frac{6}{20} = \frac{3}{10}$

5 $\frac{2}{5} \div \frac{2}{3}$

> $\frac{2}{3}$ becomes $\frac{3}{2}$

$\frac{2}{5} \times \frac{3}{2} = \frac{6}{10} = \frac{3}{5}$

> ... now multiply.

6 $\frac{2}{3} \div \frac{1}{4}$

> $\frac{1}{4}$ becomes $\frac{4}{1}$

$\frac{2}{3} \times \frac{4}{1} = \frac{8}{3} = \mathbf{2}\frac{2}{3}$

> $\frac{8}{3} = \mathbf{2}$ remainder **2**

❓ Now try these...

1 $\frac{1}{3} + \frac{1}{4} =$

2 $\frac{5}{6} - \frac{2}{3} =$

3 $\frac{7}{8} - \frac{1}{2} =$

4 $\frac{5}{9} + \frac{3}{4} =$

5 $\frac{2}{3} \times \frac{3}{5} =$

6 $\frac{8}{9} \times \frac{1}{4} =$

7 $\frac{1}{10} \div \frac{2}{5} =$

8 $\frac{3}{5} \div \frac{1}{4} =$

You need to know...

- **how to calculate fractional parts of quantities or measurements.**

We often come across fractions in everyday life, for example $\frac{1}{2}$ price sale, $\frac{1}{3}$ extra free, etc. So you need to be able to work out exactly what those fractions represent.

Always read the information you are given carefully. Then decide exactly what you are trying to find e.g. half of £32.00. In maths, 'of' means 'multiply' (**x**) so, to find 'half of £32.00' you need to calculate:

$$\frac{1}{2} \times £32.00$$

To multiply a whole number by a fraction you need to change the whole number into an improper fraction. To do this, you give it a denominator of one:

e.g. **32 as an improper fraction is $\frac{32}{1}$.**

Now you have two fractions you can multiply the numerators together and the denominators together to leave a single fraction:

e.g. $\frac{1}{2} \times \frac{32}{1} = \frac{32}{2}$

To complete the process, carry out the division:

e.g. $\frac{32}{2}$ = 16 (half of £32.00 is £16.00).

Examples

1. Calculate the sale price of this television.

$\frac{1}{2}$ of £250 $= \frac{1}{2} \times 250$

$\quad = \frac{1}{2} \times \frac{250}{1}$

$\quad = \frac{250}{2}$

$\quad = £125$

2. Calculate the total weight of this box of cereal.

$\frac{1}{3}$ of 480g $= \frac{1}{3} \times 480$

$\quad = \frac{1}{3} \times \frac{480}{1}$

$\quad = \frac{480}{3}$

$\quad = 160g$

So you get **480g + 160g = 640g**

3. Work out $\frac{3}{5}$ of £120.

$\frac{3}{5} \times £120 = \frac{3}{5} \times \frac{120}{1}$

$\quad = \frac{360}{5}$

$\quad = £72$

? Now try these...

1. The price of a car is reduced by $\frac{1}{4}$ in a sale. If the car's original price was £12 800...
   a) how much is the discount?
   b) what is the sale price?

2. A new light bulb is found to last only $\frac{3}{4}$ as long as it should. If it should have lasted 420 hours, how long does it actually last?

3. A shirt is reduced by $\frac{1}{3}$ in a sale. If it originally cost £39.00...
   a) how much is the discount?
   b) what is the sale price?

4. A school library increases its stock of books by $\frac{1}{6}$. If it had 960 books originally...
   a) how many new books has it bought?
   b) what is the new total number of books in stock?

Fractions

ℹ You need to know...

- **how to perform calculations with fractions involving mixed numbers.**

To add or subtract fractions involving mixed numbers, deal with the whole numbers first and then add or subtract the fractions (see p.13). To find the final answer, just add the results of your two calculations together.

To multiply or divide fractions involving mixed numbers, convert them to improper fractions first. Then multiply or divide the fractions as you would normally (see p.13).

Examples

① $2\frac{2}{3} + 3\frac{1}{7}$

$= (2 + 3) + (\frac{2}{3} + \frac{1}{7})$

$= 5 + (\frac{14}{21} + \frac{3}{21})$

$= 5 + \frac{17}{21}$

$= 5\frac{17}{21}$

② $4\frac{1}{2} - 1\frac{4}{5}$

$= (4 - 1) + (\frac{1}{2} - \frac{4}{5})$ Notice the + sign as we combine the two calculations.

$= 3 + (\frac{5}{10} - \frac{8}{10})$ These are the subtractions from the question.

$= 3 + (-\frac{3}{10})$

$= 3 - \frac{3}{10}$ Remember, + + − = −

$= 2\frac{7}{10}$

③ $2\frac{1}{2} \times 1\frac{1}{6}$

$= \frac{5}{2} \times \frac{7}{6}$

$= \frac{35}{12}$

$= 2\frac{11}{12}$

④ $1\frac{1}{3} \div 3\frac{1}{2}$

$= \frac{4}{3} \div \frac{7}{2}$

$= \frac{4}{3} \times \frac{2}{7}$

$= \frac{8}{21}$

❓ Now try these...

① $2\frac{1}{5} + 3\frac{2}{7}$

② $4\frac{1}{2} - 1\frac{2}{7}$

③ $5\frac{1}{4} - 2\frac{2}{3}$

④ $1\frac{2}{3} \times 3\frac{1}{9}$

⑤ $2\frac{2}{5} \div 1\frac{1}{3}$

⑥ $7\frac{1}{3} - \frac{1}{6}$

⑦ $\frac{1}{8} + 3\frac{3}{4}$

⑧ $5\frac{1}{2} \times 2$

⑨ $5\frac{1}{2} \div 2$

⑩ $2\frac{1}{2} \div 2\frac{6}{12}$

✓ You should already know...

- how the place table can be extended for decimals
- that terminating decimals have an exact value
- that recurring decimals have digits or sequences of digits that repeat without end.

ⓘ You also need to know...

- how to add and subtract decimals of up to two decimal places.

When adding or subtracting decimals you use the same method as for whole numbers.

Before you begin, make sure the decimal points are lined up and put in zeros to fill any gaps.

Always start with the column on the right-hand side (in the examples shown below, that's the Hundredths ($\frac{1}{100}$) column) and don't forget to bring down the decimal point!

Examples

①

H	T	U	$\frac{1}{10}$	$\frac{1}{100}$

```
  3 4 2 . 7 9
+   1 7 . 6 0
      1   1
  ─────────────
  3 6 0 . 3 9
```

Add the **0** if it helps. **9 + 0 = 9**. Write **9** in the Hundredths column

7 + 6 = 13. Write **3** in the Tenths column and carry **1** into the Units column. Don't forget to bring down the decimal point!

2 + 7 + 1 = 10. Write **0** in the Units column and carry **1** into the Tens column

4 + 1 + 1 = 6. Write **6** in the Tens column

3 + 0 = 3. Write **3** in the Hundreds column

②

T	U	$\frac{1}{10}$	$\frac{1}{100}$

```
   4  13    1
   5  4 . 1 7
 - 1  8 . 2 5
   ─────────────
   3  5 . 9 2
```

7 – 5 = 2. Write **2** in the Hundredths column

Borrow **1** from the Units column to give **11 – 2 = 9.** Write **9** in the Tenths column

Borrow **1** from the Tens column to give **13 – 8 = 5.** Write **5** in the Units column

4 – 1 = 3. Write **3** in the Tens column

? Now try these...

1
```
    8 3 . 1
+   1 0 . 1
```

4
```
  1 8 9 . 5
+   1 8 . 7 2
```

7
```
  1 1 1 . 1 1
+   9 9 . 9 9
```

10
```
  2 0 9 . 9 9
-   3 2 . 6 9
```

2
```
  1 0 0 . 5
+   5 6 . 5
```

5
```
  1 0 9 2 . 5
-   1 9 9 . 4
```

8
```
  1 1 1 . 1 1
-   9 9 . 9 9
```

11
```
  4 0 6 7 . 3
+   1 4 1 . 7
```

3
```
  5 4 2 . 9
-   1 0 0 . 6
```

6
```
  5 0 7 5 . 1 6
-   3 0 1 . 0 8
```

9
```
  3 2 9 . 6 3
-   5 6 . 6 2
```

12
```
  1 3 5 4 . 6
-   1 2 3 . 0 2
```

Decimals

You need to know...

- **how to understand and use decimals and negative numbers.**

A common use of decimals is in dealing with money and bank accounts. Sums of money are written to 2 decimal places (2 d.p). The whole numbers represent pounds and the decimals represent pence.

Money that is put into an account is called a **credit**. Money taken out is called a **debit** (or a withdrawal). Withdrawals normally appear as negative numbers. The amount of money remaining in the account is called the **balance**. If a sum of money larger than the balance is taken out, the new balance will be negative.

Examples

Look at this bank statement:

1. How much money was in the account at the beginning of June?
   £221.59

2. How much money was received as a salary in June?
   £550.00

3. After the CHQ00031 transaction, was the account balance positive or negative?
   Negative

4. If no more transactions take place before 6 July what will the account balance be after July's salary of £550.00 is recieved?
   -£139.78 + £550.00 = £410.22

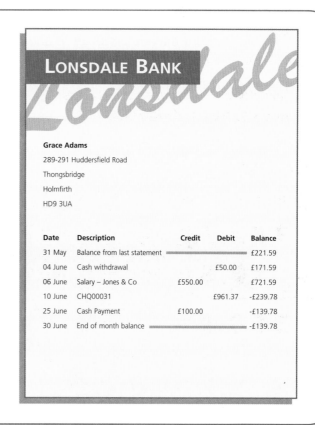

LONSDALE BANK

Grace Adams
289-291 Huddersfield Road
Thongsbridge
Holmfirth
HD9 3UA

Date	Description	Credit	Debit	Balance
31 May	Balance from last statement			£221.59
04 June	Cash withdrawal		£50.00	£171.59
06 June	Salary – Jones & Co	£550.00		£721.59
10 June	CHQ00031		£961.37	-£239.78
25 June	Cash Payment	£100.00		-£139.78
30 June	End of month balance			-£139.78

Now try these...

1. Write the following amounts as pounds and pence using decimals:
   a) three pounds and fifty pence
   b) eleven pounds and two pence
   c) one hundred and fifty pence
   d) two hundred and one pence
   e) nine hundred pounds and seventy pence
   f) twenty three pounds and twenty three pence

2. David receives a bank statement saying he is overdrawn by twenty five pounds and fifty pence.
   a) write this number as it would appear on the statement.
   b) how much money does David need to pay into the account to take the balance to...
      i) £0.00? ii) £10.00? iii) £50.00?

ℹ You need to know...

- **how to multiply and divide decimals by 10, 100 and 1000.**

To **multiply** a decimal by 10, the digits remain the same but you move the decimal point one place to the **right**. To multiply by 100, you move the decimal point two places to the right. To multiply by 1000, you move it three places etc…

The trick is to count the number of zeros and then move the decimal point to the right by the same number of places.

In the same way, to **divide** a decimal by 10, 100 or 1000 you move the decimal point to the **left** by one, two or three places.

Examples

1 Multiply 21.375 by 10, 100 and 1000.

$$21.375 \times 10 = 213.75$$
$$21.375 \times 100 = 2137.5$$
$$21.375 \times 1000 = 21375.0$$

> There's no need for the decimal point in the last example, but you can put it in if it helps.

2 Multiply 425.6 by 10, 100 and 1000.

$$425.6 \div 10 = 42.56$$
$$425.6 \div 100 = 4.256$$
$$425.6 \div 1000 = 0.4256$$

> You need a **zero** here to show there's no whole number.

3 Divide 68.75 by 10, 100 and 1000.

$$068.75 \div 1000 = 0.06875$$

> This **zero** is vital. Without it all the place values would change.

❓ Now try these...

1. Multiply 25.189 by 10, 100 and 1000
2. Divide 13.27 by 10, 100 and 1000
3. Multiply 0.0135 by 10, 100 and 1000
4. Divide 475.6 by 10, 100 and 1000
5. Multiply 1.111 by 10, 100 and 1000
6. Divide 1.111 by 10, 100 and 1000
7. Multiply 63.98 by 100 and then divide by 1000. What is the answer?

Decimals

You need to know...

- **how to multiply and divide decimals of up to two decimal places by whole numbers**
- **how to multiply decimals of up to two decimal places by other decimals.**

The method for multiplying and dividing decimals by a whole number is the same as for multiplying or dividing two whole numbers (see p.6). You just need to remember to bring the decimal point up/down to your answer and line it up with the decimal point in the question.

To multiply two decimals together, treat them as whole numbers and perform the multiplication as you would normally. When you have an answer, put the decimal point in position by counting the total number of decimal places in the original numbers.

Examples

1
```
   39.28
x      6
  5 1 4
 235.68
```

2
```
      8
x   0.5
   4.0
```

3
```
   2.73
x    18
  2730
  21 8 4
   5
   1
  49.14
```

4
```
      04.06
  8)32.48
    32
     048
      48
       0
```

5
```
      02.2
  6)13.2
    12
     12
     12
      0
```

6
```
      01.6
 12)19.2
    12
     72
     72
      0
```

7
```
   7.56
x  9.2
```

Remove the decimal points...

```
      756
x      92
   6 8 0 4 0
    5   5
   1 5 1 2
      1 1
   6 9.5 5 2
       3 2 1
```

Now count the total number of decimal places in the question. **7.56** has **2** decimal places and **9.2** has 1 decimal place, making a total of **3**. So, the answer is **69.552**.

ℹ️ You need to know...

- **how to divide decimals of up to two decimal places by other decimals.**

The easiest way to divide a decimal by another decimal is to turn the number you are dividing by into a whole number. To do this, multiply both numbers in the calculation by 10 or 100 (depending on how many decimal places the divider has).

As long as you do the same to both numbers, your final answer will not be affected.

Remember: to multiply by 10, you need to move the decimal point one place to the right. To multiply by 100, you move it two places to the right.

Once you have done this, divide the numbers as before (see p.6). Just make sure you bring the decimal point up to the answer and line it up with the decimal point in the question (if there is one).

Examples

① 1.92 ÷ 1.2

1.92 x 10 = 19.2
1.2 x 10 = 12

Multiply both numbers by 10

```
        0 1 . 6
  12 ) 1 9 . 2
       1 2
       ─────
         7 2
         7 2
         ─────
           0
```

Now divide as normal

② 45.2 ÷ 0.5

45.2 x 10 = 452
0.5 x 10 = 5

Multiply both numbers by 10

```
        0 9 0 . 4
   5 ) 4 5 2 . 0
       4 5
       ─────
         0 2 0
           2 0
           ─────
             0
```

Now divide as normal

❓ Now try these...

①
```
  1 3 . 6
x       5
```

②
```
  2 2 . 4 8
x         7
```

③
```
  1 5 8 . 4
x       3 . 6
```

④
```
  2 9 . 5 8
x   0 . 4 2
```

⑤ 8) 68.48

⑥ 14) 2.24

⑦ 1.8) 6.48

⑧ 0.3) 1.335

⑨ 0.25) 5.5

⑩ 0.1) 99.9

⑪ 1.25) 4.25

Decimals

Examples

Work out the following…

(1) 24 x 0.6

$$\begin{array}{r} 2\,4 \\ \times \quad 0_2 6 \\ \hline 1\,4\,4 \end{array}$$

$$= 14.4$$

> Multiply decimals as you would whole numbers

> Now count the digits after the decimal point in the numbers being multiplied and transfer to the answer (0.6 = 1 decimal place).

(2) 15 x 0.03

$$\begin{array}{r} 1\,5 \\ \times \quad _1 3 \\ \hline 4\,5 \end{array}$$

$$= 0.45$$

(3) 24 ÷ 0.6

240 ÷ 6

$$\begin{array}{r} 4\,0.0 \\ 6\overline{)2\,4\,0\,.0} \end{array}$$

$$= 40$$

> Multiply both numbers by 10 to make the number doing the dividing a whole number.

> Then divide as you would whole numbers. Remember to take the decimal point up to the answer.

(4) 15 ÷ 0.03

$$\begin{array}{r} 0\,5\,0\,0 \\ 3\overline{)1\,5\,0\,0} \end{array}$$

$$= 500$$

You need to know…

- **how to multiply and divide by a number between 0 and 1.**

When a number is **multiplied** by a value between 0 and 1, the answer is **smaller** than the original value. However, when a number is **divided** by a value between 0 and 1 the answer is **bigger** than the original value.

? Now try these…

For each question, state whether the answer will be bigger or smaller than the original value. Then use a calculator to see if you were right.

1. 16 x 0.3
2. 17 ÷ 0.5
3. 215 x 0.007
4. 218 ÷ 0.8
5. 1234 ÷ 0.005
6. 3217 x 0.0102
7. 479 x 0.794
8. 6 x 0.5
9. 596 ÷ 0.25
10. 596 x 0.25
11. 8673 ÷ 0.72
12. 1 x 0.75
13. 105 ÷ 0.3
14. 5793 ÷ 0.2

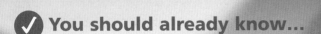

✅ You should already know...

- that 'percentage' means 'number of parts per 100'.

ℹ You also need to know...

- how to find the exact amount or quantity represented by a percentage.

Percentages are another kind of number that you frequently come across in everyday life, e.g. 50% extra free, 40% off marked price. To understand them, you need to be able to calculate the exact amounts the percentages represent.

Start by writing the percentage as a fraction. Once you have done that, find the fraction of the whole.

Remember that 'of' means 'multiply' (×).

? Now try these...

1 Calculate...
  a) 85% of £600.   **c)** 4% of 750ml.
  b) 25% of 250g?   **d)** 98% of 100m.

2 A holiday is reduced by 30% in a last-minute offer. If the cost was originally £2400 work out the saving and the actual cost of the holiday.

3 The weekly attendance of supporters at a football club is increased by 15%. If 1200 people attended originally, how many more people are now attending and what is the new attendance?

Examples

1

What will this shirt cost after the reduction?

> 40% of £9 means $\frac{40}{100} \times £9$

$\frac{40}{100} \times £9 = \frac{40}{100} \times \frac{9}{1} = \frac{360}{100} = £3.60$ saved

The shirt will cost **£9 – £3.60 = £5.40**

2

What is the total weight of this cheese?

> 50% of 350g means $\frac{50}{100} \times 350$

$\frac{50}{100} \times 350 = \frac{50}{100} \times \frac{350}{1} = \frac{17\,500}{100} = 175g$

So the cheese weighs **350g + 175g = 525g**

3

What is 45% of £1.80?

> 45% of £1.80 means $\frac{45}{100} \times 180p$ (£1.80 = 180p)

$\frac{45}{100} \times 180 = \frac{45}{100} \times \frac{180}{1} = \frac{8100}{100} = 81p$

Percentages

ℹ️ You need to know...

- **how to express an amount or quantity as a percentage of another**
- **how to use percentages to compare quantities.**

Any quantity that represents part of a whole e.g. '8 out of 10', can be written as a percentage.

Start by writing the numbers as a fraction. The number that represents the whole always goes on the bottom e.g. $\frac{8}{10}$

Then multiply the fraction by 100%. Remember, when you multiply a fraction by a whole number you change the whole number into an improper fraction first (see p.12) e.g. $\frac{8}{10} \times \frac{100}{1} = \frac{800}{10} = 80\%$

Percentages are a good way of comparing different amounts or quantities, because the 0-100% scale is easy to understand. Percentages also provide a useful way of describing increases and decreases.

Examples

1 Express 200m as a percentage of 4km.

> The units must be the same, so convert **4km** into **m** (see p.62): **4 x 1000m = 4000m**

> '**200m out of 4000m**' is $\frac{200}{4000}$

$$\frac{200}{4000} \times \frac{100}{1} = \frac{20\,000}{4000} = 5\%$$

2 A box of cereal weighs 320g. As part of a special offer, its weight is increased to 400g. Express this increase as a percentage of the original weight.

> First calculate the actual increase:

400g – 320g = 80g

> So, you need to find **80g** out of **320g** as a percentage:

$$\frac{80}{320} \times \frac{100}{1} = \frac{8000}{320} = 25\%$$

3 A man buys a radio for £20. After a year, he sells it on the internet for £12.50. Calculate the loss (decrease) as a percentage of the original cost.

> Calculate the actual loss:

£20.00 – £12.50 = £7.50

> Then the percentage loss:

$$\frac{£7.50}{£20.00} \times \frac{100}{1} = \frac{750}{20} = 37.5\%$$

❓ Now try these...

1 Express 42 as a percentage of 210.

2 Express 12cm as a percentage of 120cm.

3 Express 330ml as a percentage of 1000ml.

4 A student gets 36 out of a possible 80 marks in Maths and 24 out of a possible 60 marks in Science.
  a) Express these results as percentages.
  b) Which subject did they do best in?

5 A jockey weighs in at 63kg. He has to get down to 56kg for an important race. What is this decrease in weight as a percentage?

6 A 25g bag of crisps contains 5g of fat. What is this as a percentage?

7 An antique clock is bought for £5000. It is later sold for £5400. What is the profit (increase) as a percentage?

Examples

1

A CD player is priced at £50 + VAT. What is the total price to be paid?

17.5% of £50 is $\frac{17.5}{100} \times \frac{50}{1} = \frac{875}{100} = £8.75$

So, the total cost of the CD player is...
£50 + £8.75 = £58.75

You need to know...

- **how to solve problems involving VAT and simple interest.**

Value Added Tax (VAT) is payable on most goods we buy. Often it is included in the price. Sometimes, however, it needs to be added on to find the total cost of the product. In the UK, VAT is currently calculated as 17.5% of the product's value.

Interest is an additional sum of money, paid to you for investing money (e.g. putting it into a bank account) or charged to you for borrowing money over a period of time.

Simple interest means that the amount of interest paid each year is calculated from the original sum of money invested or borrowed.

2

Mrs Mears wins £1000 and puts it into an account that pays 6% interest per year. If she leaves it there, how much money will she have in the account after 2 years?

6% of £1000 is $\frac{6}{100} \times \frac{1000}{1} = \frac{6000}{100} = £60$ interest per year.

> With simple interest the interest gained (**£60**) is not added to the amount invested so it does not earn interest in the next year.

So, after 2 years she has...
£1000 + £60 + £60 = £1120

original sum   1st year's interest   2nd year's interest

? Now try these...

1. A DVD player is advertised as costing £90 + VAT. What is the total price to be paid?
2. A phone company charges 5p per minute for calls to the USA, plus VAT. What is the total cost for a call lasting 20 minutes?
3. Louise invests £3500 in an account paying 5% interest per annum (per annum means 'each year'). If she leaves the money there, how much money will she have in the account after 3 years?

Percentages

You need to know...

- **how to find and use equivalent fractions, decimals and percentages.**

It will help you a great deal if you learn the equivalent decimal and percentage values for the most common fractions.

You will come across lots of different fractions, decimals and percentages though so, it is important you know how to convert from one to another.

The chart below, shows the rules you need to follow.

Fraction	Decimal	Percentage
1	1.0	100%
$\frac{3}{4}$	0.75	75%
$\frac{1}{2}$	0.5	50%
$\frac{1}{3}$	0.3	33%
$\frac{1}{4}$	0.25	25%
$\frac{1}{5}$	0.2	20%
$\frac{1}{10}$	0.1	10%

Example

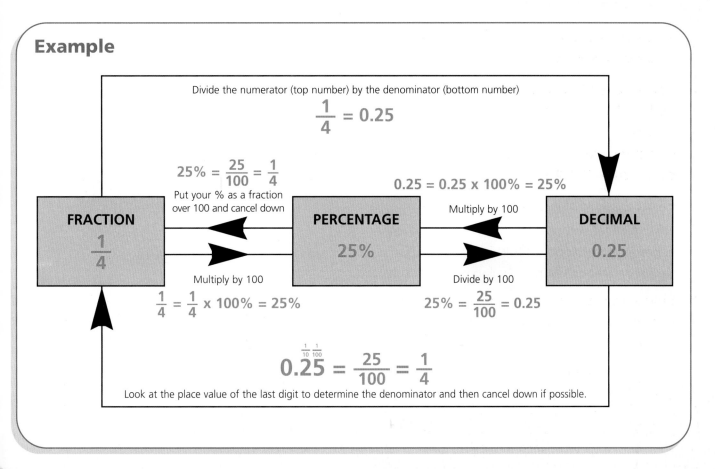

Divide the numerator (top number) by the denominator (bottom number)

$$\frac{1}{4} = 0.25$$

$$25\% = \frac{25}{100} = \frac{1}{4}$$

Put your % as a fraction over 100 and cancel down

$$0.25 = 0.25 \times 100\% = 25\%$$

Multiply by 100

| FRACTION $\frac{1}{4}$ | PERCENTAGE 25% | DECIMAL 0.25 |

Multiply by 100

$$\frac{1}{4} = \frac{1}{4} \times 100\% = 25\%$$

Divide by 100

$$25\% = \frac{25}{100} = 0.25$$

$$0.\overset{\frac{1}{10}\frac{1}{100}}{25} = \frac{25}{100} = \frac{1}{4}$$

Look at the place value of the last digit to determine the denominator and then cancel down if possible.

Now try these...

1. Convert $\frac{3}{5}$ to a decimal and then a percentage.
2. What is 65% as a fraction and a decimal?
3. Express 0.32 as a percentage and as a fraction simplified to its lowest terms.
4. Convert $\frac{3}{8}$ to a decimal and then to a percentage.
5. Re-write 36% as a fraction in its lowest terms and as a decimal.
6. Give 1.25 as a percentage and as a mixed number (fraction).

Examples

1 A shirt is in a sale where everything has been reduced by 15%. If the sale price of the shirt is £6.80, what was its original price?

> Don't work out 15% of £6.80 – it would be wrong!

The sale price is 100% – 15% = 85% of the original price. So, you need to work out...

£6.80 ÷ 85 = £0.08

> £0.08 is 1% of the original price.

Therefore...

100% = 100 x £0.08 = £8.00

2 A couple sell their house for £135 000, making a profit of 20% on what they originally paid. What did they pay for the house?

£135 000 represents 100% + 20% = 120% of the original price. So, you need to work out...

£135 000 ÷ 120 = £1 125

> £1 125 is 1% of the original price.

Therefore...

100% = 100 x 1 125 = £112 500

ℹ You need to know...

- **how to identify which number represents the whole in problems involving percentages.**

When solving problems involving percentages, it is essential that you correctly identify which number represents the whole or 100%. If you get this wrong, all the following calculations and results will be wrong too!

In particular, watch out for questions involving percentages where you are asked to calculate the original amount.

? Now try these...

1 A new car depreciates (loses value) by 10% over a year. If it is worth £6 750 at the end of the first year, what was the original value of the car?

2 An electrical store reduces all its stock by 25%. The price of a television in the sale is £240. What was its original price?

3 A coat costs £90 in a shop sale. This is a 20% reduction on its original price. A week later the price is lowered even further, to 30% off the original price. What is the new sale price of the coat?

4 Anya's new job pays £12 750 p.a. This is a 2% increase on her old salary. What was her old salary?

Percentages

ℹ You need to know...

- **how to solve problems involving compound interest.**

You have already done calculations involving simple interest where the interest earned each year is the same (see p.24). There is another kind of interest called **compound interest**. This is where the interest earned in a year is added to the original amount of money, and the next year's interest is calculated from the new total.

With compound interest, the percentage of interest earned remains the same, however the total amount of money in the bank account increases each year and so the interest paid increases too.

You might be asked to calculate what the final total is after several years. In situations like this, it can be quicker to use decimal multipliers than percentages.

? Now try these...

1. £2500 is invested at 8% compound interest for 3 years. What is the final value of the investment?

2. A bank offers two different savings plans: 5% simple interest or 4% compound interest. If you invest £2000, which offers the best payout after...
   a) 10 years
   b) 20 years.

Example

£1000 is invested at 4% compound interest for 3 years. Calculate the amount in the account at the end of this period.

Year 1
4% interest = $\frac{4}{100}$ x 1000 = £40
Total = £1000 + £40 = £1040

Year 2
4% interest = $\frac{4}{100}$ x 1040 = £41.60
Total = £1040 + £41.60 = £1081.60

Year 3
4% interest = $\frac{4}{100}$ x 1081.60 = £43.26
Total = £1081.60 + £43.26 = **£1124.86**

To find the total at the end of each year, the interest (4%) is added to the sum of money already in the account (100%). This could have been calculated more efficiently...

100% + 4% = 104%   Total for Year

Expressed as a decimal this is 1.04 ($\frac{104}{100}$ = 1.04). So, 1.04 is your decimal multiplier.

£1000 x 1.04 = £1040	Total for Year 1
£1040 x 1.04 = £1081.60	Total for Year 2
£1081.60 x 1.04 = £1124.86	Total for Year 3

These calculations can be simplified even further...

£1000 x 1.04 x 1.04 x 1.04 = £1124.86
£1000 x 1.04^3 = £1124.86

Original Amount   Decimal Multiplier   Number of Years

There is £1124.86 in the account at the end of the third year.

Everyday Calculations

ℹ️ You need to know...

- **how to compare quantities and amounts efficiently.**

When you go shopping, the same product is often available in a variety of sizes at different prices. To find out which one offers the best value for money, you need to be able to make accurate comparisons between them.

Likewise, if you require a service like a plumber, window cleaner, taxi etc. you will find that different companies have different rates and fixed costs. Again, you need to be able to determine which company offers the best value for money if you don't want to be short changed!

Examples

① Uncle Don's Meat Pies are available in two sizes: 300g and 500g. If a 300g pie costs £1.26 and a 500g pie costs £1.95. Which offers the best value for money?

Work out how much 100g of each pie costs...

$$\frac{300g}{100g} = 3 \quad \text{SO} \quad \frac{£1.26}{3} = 0.42 \quad \text{i.e. 42p per 100g}$$

$$\frac{500g}{100g} = 5 \quad \text{SO} \quad \frac{£1.95}{5} = 0.39 \quad \text{i.e. 39p per 100g}$$

The 500g pies are the best value.

② Mark's Taxis charge a fixed amount of £3 per journey, plus £2 per mile. Helen's Cabs only charge a fixed amount of £1, but £2.50 per mile. Work out which taxi company is the cheapest for journeys of 1, 2, 3, 4, 5 and 10 miles.

Journey (miles)	Mark's Taxis	Helen's Cabs
1	(1 x £2) + £3 = **£5.00**	(1 x £2.50) + £1 = **£3.50**
2	(2 x £2) + £3 = **£7.00**	(2 x £2.50) + £1 = **£6.00**
3	(3 x £2) + £3 = **£9.00**	(3 x £2.50) + £1 = **£8.50**
4	(4 x £2) + £3 = **£11.00**	(4 x £2.50) + £1 = **£11.00**
5	(5 x £2) + £3 = **£13.00**	(5 x £2.50) + £1 = **£13.50**
10	(10 x £2) + £3 = **£23.00**	(10 x £2.50) + £1 = **£26.00**

Both taxi companies charge the same amount for a 4 mile journey.

❓ Now try these...

① A supermarket sells lemonade in 2 litre bottles and 3 litre bottles. If 2 litre bottles cost 61p and 3 litre bottles cost 84p which offers the best value?

② Katie the Plumber charges a £50 call out fee, plus £15 per hour. Perfect Pipes charges a £60 call out fee, plus £12 per hour.

   a) Work out the cost for each plumber to do 1, 2, 3, 4, 5 and 6 hours' work.

   b) Who would be the cheapest for a 3 hour job?

   c) Who would be the cheapest for a 7 hour job?

Order of Operations

You need to know...

- the correct order in which to carry out mathematical operations when solving problems
- how to use brackets correctly.

When a calculation involves more than one operation, you must carry them out in the correct order – this is not necessarily the order in which they appear.

BIDMAS

Brackets

Indices (or powers)

Divisions and **M**ultiplications (in any order)

Additions and **S**ubtractions (in any order)

Putting brackets into a calculation tells people that they need to perform that part of the calculation before anything else. It can make a big difference to the final answer so make sure you put them in the right place!

Examples

① $7 + 3 \times 2$ — Do the multiplication first so, $3 \times 2 = 6$ ...

$7 + 6 = 13$ — ... and then the addition

② $14 - (6 + 3)$ — Do the brackets first so, $6 + 3 = 9$ ...

$14 - 9 = 5$ — ... and then the subtraction

③ $3^2 \times (6 - 4)$ — Do the brackets first so, $6 - 4 = 2$ ...

$3^2 \times 2$ — ... then the square, $3^2 = 9$ ...

$9 \times 2 = 18$ — ... and then the multiplication

④ $\dfrac{5 - 17}{2 \times 3}$ — A divide line like this makes the numerator and denominator act as if they were in brackets, so do them first before dividing

$\dfrac{5 - 17}{6}$ — Do the multiplication first so, $2 \times 3 = 6$ ...

... then the subtraction, $5 - 17 = -12$ ...

$\dfrac{-12}{6} = -2$ — ... and then the division

Now try these...

Calculate...

1. $8 - 3 \times 2$
2. $15 - (2 + 4)$
3. $5^2 - 2 \times (4 - 1)$
4. $\dfrac{5 + 11}{12 - 2^2}$
5. $7 - 4 \times 3 + 2$
6. $7 \times 4 - 3 \times 2$

7. $13 - 3 \times 4 + 3$

Put the brackets into this calculation so that the answer is ...

a) 43
b) 70
c) 4

ℹ️ You need to know...

- **how to enter complex calculations into your calculator using brackets.**

If you tried to type a whole calculation into your calculator as it appears on a page it would do each part of the calculation as you typed it. However, we know that multiplication and division should be carried out before addition and subtraction in the order of operations (see p.29). This is where the bracket functions on a calculator become useful. The bracket [(... ...)] functions enable a calculation to be entered in one go.

Example

Use your calculator to work out $\dfrac{32 + 16}{105 - 3^2}$

Key in... [(...] **32 + 16** [...)] ÷

[(...] **105 − 3** x^2 [...)]

= ⬜⬜⬜⬜⬜**0.5**

❓ Now try these...

Use the bracket functions on your calculator to perform these calculations.

1. 32 x (7 + 12)

2. $\dfrac{50}{2 \times 8}$

3. $\dfrac{9 - 18}{32}$

4. $\dfrac{64 - 1100}{83 - 4714}$

Order of Operations

ℹ You need to know...

- **how to solve problems involving powers and roots.**

These are the rules when it comes to dealing with indices...

To multiply, add the indices	$3^7 \times 3^2 = 3^{7+2} = 3^9$
To divide, subtract the indices	$\dfrac{3^7}{3^2} = 3^{7-2} = 3^5$
To raise a power to another power, multiply the indices	$(3^7)^2 = 3^{7 \times 2} = 3^{14}$
Any number to the power of 1 is simply the number itself	$3^1 = 3$
Any number to the power of 0 is 1	$3^0 = 1$
Any number to a negative power means 1 divided by that number to the positive power	$3^{-2} = \dfrac{1}{3^2}$
A fractional power is a root. A power of $\frac{1}{2}$ means square root, a power of $\frac{1}{3}$ means cube root	$3^{\frac{1}{2}} = \sqrt{3} \qquad 3^{\frac{1}{3}} = \sqrt[3]{3}$
If a fractional power has a numerator greater than 1, the root is raised to the power of that number	$3^{\frac{2}{3}} = (\sqrt[3]{3})^2$

❓ Now try these...

1. Simplify...

   a) $4^8 \times 4^6$ b) $\dfrac{5^9}{5^7}$ c) $(7^3)^4$ d) 3^0 e) 4^{-3}

   f) $2^2 \times 2^9$ g) $\dfrac{7^7}{7^4}$ h) $(9^6)^2$ i) 6^{-3} j) $5^1 \times 5^2 \times 5^3$

2. a) Work out... i) $(\sqrt{4})^3$ ii) $\sqrt{(4^3)}$

   b) What do you notice about the answers to **a)**? What does this tell you?

3. Rewrite the following using root symbols...

   a) $4^{\frac{1}{2}}$ b) $6^{\frac{3}{2}}$ c) $7^{\frac{3}{3}}$ d) $10^{\frac{1}{3}}$ e) $5^{\frac{2}{5}}$

i You need to know...

- **what a ratio is**
- **how to simplify a ratio.**

A ratio is a means of comparing two or more related quantities.

Ratios are usually only written with whole numbers. A colon (:) is used to separate the different quantities.

For example, in one week, the ratio of working weekdays to weekend days is **5 : 2**, since there are 5 weekdays and 2 weekend days. The colon is read as 'to' so, 5 : 2 is read as 'five to two'.

Ratios can be simplified in a similar way to fractions, but you must remember that fractions and ratios are different – they give different information about a situation.

In the example above, the ratio of weekdays to weekend days is 5 : 2. However, the fraction of weekdays is $\frac{5}{7}$ and the fraction of weekend days is $\frac{2}{7}$ as there are 7 days in a week.

FEBRUARY

Monday	Tuesday	Wednesday	Thursday	Friday	Saturday	Sunday
1	2	3	4	5	6	7
8	9	10	11	12	13	14
15	16	17	18	19	20	21
22	23	24	25	26	27	28

Examples

1 Simplify the ratio 10 : 6.

As long as you divide both parts of the ratio by the same number, the meaning of the ratio will stay the same.

$$÷2 \left(\begin{array}{c} \mathbf{10 : 6} \\ \mathbf{= 5 : 3} \end{array} \right) ÷2$$

> **2** is a common factor of **10** and **6**, so divide both numbers by **2**

2 In a pile of bricks, there are 15 red ones and 5 yellow ones.

a) What is the ratio of red to yellow bricks?

$$\begin{array}{c} \mathbf{red : yellow} \\ ÷5 \left(\begin{array}{c} \mathbf{15 : 5} \\ \mathbf{= 3 : 1} \end{array} \right) ÷5 \end{array}$$

> **5** is a common factor of **15** and **5**, so divide both numbers by **5**

b) What is the ratio of yellow to red bricks?

$$\begin{array}{c} \mathbf{yellow : red} \\ ÷5 \left(\begin{array}{c} \mathbf{5 : 15} \\ \mathbf{= 1 : 3} \end{array} \right) ÷5 \end{array}$$

> Put the items in the ratio in the same order they are written

3 In a maths class, $\frac{2}{5}$ of the pupils are boys. What is the ratio of boys to girls?

$$\begin{array}{c} \mathbf{boys : girls} \\ \mathbf{2 : 3} \\ (\text{not } 2 : 5!) \end{array}$$

> If $\frac{2}{5}$ are boys then $\frac{3}{5}$ must be girls.

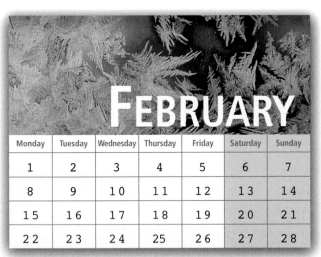

? Now try these...

1 Simplify the following ratios:

a) 6 : 2   **b)** 9 : 18   **c)** 25 : 10   **d)** 3 : 12

e) 32 : 8 : 16   **f)** 4 : 16 : 8   **g)** 9 : 27 : 45

2 $\frac{4}{7}$ of Anna's toy animals are farm animals, the rest are zoo animals.

a) What is the ratio of farm animals to zoo animals?

b) What is the ratio of zoo animals to farm animals?

Ratio and Proportion

ℹ You need to know...

- **how to solve problems involving ratio using the unitary method.**

It is often useful to reduce a ratio into the form **n : 1** or **1 : n**, where n is any number (an integer or decimal). These are called **unitary ratios** and they clearly show how many times bigger or smaller one part is in comparison to the other.

Scales on maps and scale drawings (see p.76) are often written as unitary ratios. It makes calculating actual lengths and distances much easier.

To express a ratio in the form n : 1, divide both parts of the ratio by the number on the right-hand side.

To express a ratio in the form 1 : n, divide both parts of the ratio by the number on the left-hand side.

Examples

1 a) Lawn seed is mixed from fescue seed and rye seed in the ratio 8 : 34. Express this ratio in the form 1 : n.

÷8 (**8 : 34** / **1 : 4.25**) ÷8   Divide both sides by 8

b) A garden centre buys 4 sacks of fescue seed to make the lawn mix. How many sacks of rye seed do they need?

The ratio shows that for every unit of fescue seed you need 4.25 times that amount of rye seed.

4 sacks x 4.25 = 17 sacks

The garden centre need to the mix 4 sacks of fescue seed with **17 sacks of rye seed**.

2 A builder uses a mortar made from 8 parts sand to 3 parts cement.

a) What is the ratio of sand to cement? Express this in the form n : 1.

The ratio of sand to cement is 8 : 3

÷3 (**8 : 3** / **2.6 : 1**) ÷3   Divide both sides by 3

b) The builder has 50kg of cement to make mortar with. How much sand does he need?

The ratio shows us that for every unit of cement you need 2.6 times that amount of sand.

50kg x 2.6 = 130kg

The builder needs to mix **130kg of sand** with the 50kg of concrete.

❓ Now try these...

1 Write these ratios in the form 1 : n.
a) 2 : 11   **b)** 3 : 17
c) 0.5 : 6.2   (You'll need to multiply this one)

2 Write these ratios in the form n : 1.
a) 7 : 4   **b)** 5 : 3   **c)** 1 : 8

3 Mira changed £30.00 into euros at the foreign exchange. She was given 48 euros in return for her money. Express the exchange rate of pounds to euro as a ratio in the form 1 : n.

4 Kevin is making a big jug of orange squash for his friends. The instructions tell him to mix 4 parts of cordial with 10 parts of water.
a) Express these quantities as a ratio in the form 1 : n.
b) The bottle of cordial is 1.5 litres. If Kevin uses all the cordial how much water will he need?

You need to know...

- **how to solve simple problems involving ratio and direct proportion.**

Because the numbers in a ratio represent parts in a whole, a ratio can tell you how to share something out or divide it up.

In simple terms, if you had 5 sweets and were told to share them between you and a friend in the ratio of 3 : 2, you would get 3 of the 5 sweets and your friend would get 2.

Ratios are also very useful when you need to increase or decrease quantities whilst keeping the proportions the same.

Examples

1

Mavis and Albert enter a prize draw. Mavis buys 5 tickets and Albert buys 3. They agree to share any prize money in the ratio of the number of tickets bought. How much money would each person receive if they won £240?

The ratio of tickets bought is...

Mavis : Albert

   5 : 3

Add together to find the total number of tickets bought

5 + 3 = 8 tickets

£240 ÷ 8 = £30

prize money per ticket

Therefore...

Mavis receives 5 x £30 = £150
Albert receives 3 x £30 = £90

Check your answer
£150 + £90 = £240

2 Auntie Edna makes her famous '2, 4, 6, 8' cake using the recipe alongside. The recipe makes enough cake for 12 people. How much of each ingredient would be needed to make enough cake for 18 people?

'2 4 6 8' CAKE
2 eggs mixed with
2 cups of milk
400g margarine
600g sugar
800g flour

Start with the ratio **12 : 18**

You could divide the quantities by **12** to find the amount needed for one person and then multiply it by **18**. However, this would be tricky without a calculator.

To make things easier, simplify the ratio:

÷6　**12 : 18**　÷6
   = 2 : 3

6 is a common factor of **12** and **18**, so divide both numbers by **6**:

Now, divide each quantity by **2** and then multiply by **3**:

2 eggs	(÷ 2 x 3 =)	**3 eggs**
2 cups of milk	(÷ 2 x 3 =)	**3 cups of milk**
400g margarine	(÷ 2 x 3 =)	**600g margarine**
600g sugar	(÷ 2 x 3 =)	**900g sugar**
800g flour	(÷ 2 x 3 =)	**1200g flour**

Now try these...

1 Three boys aged 6, 8 and 10 share out their sweets in the ratio of their ages. If they have 36 sweets in total, how many does each boy get?

2 A pudding which serves 8 people requires 200g of dried mixed fruit and 300g of sugar. What quantity of each of these ingredients would be needed to make enough pudding for just 6 people?

Ratio and Proportion

1 A new car costs £9500. Each year it will depreciate (go down) in value by 15%. What is the car worth after 2 years?

Value of car at end of year 1:
100% – 15% = 85%
85% of £9500 = $\frac{85}{100}$ x 9500 = £8075

Value of car at end of year 2:
85% of £8075 = $\frac{85}{100}$ x 8075 = **£6863.75**

These calculations are quicker if you use a decimal multiplier:

£9500 x 0.85 = £8075   85% = $\frac{85}{100}$ = 0.85
£8075 x 0.85 = £6863.75

This can be simplified even further...

£9500 x 0.85 x 0.85 = £6863.75
£9500 x 0.85² = £6863.75

Original Amount   Decimal Multiplier   Number of Years

2 A new shop makes £5000 profit in the first month it opens. The owner hopes the profits will rise by 5% a month in the first year. If they do rise at this rate, what will the profits be after the next 5 months?

In this problem, the current profit (£5000) represents 100%. Therefore, the total profit at the end of a month is 100% + 5% = 105%.

105% = $\frac{105}{100}$ = 1.05   This is the decimal multiplier

To find the total after 5 months, multiply the original amount by 1.05 to the power of 5 (1.05⁵):

£5000 x 1.05⁵ = £6381.41 to 2 d.p.

---

i You need to know...

- **how to calculate the result of a proportional change using only multiplicative methods.**

You have seen that a decimal multiplier can be used to calculate compound interest quickly and efficiently (see p.27). The same method can be used to calculate the results of any proportional change where the percentage increase or decrease remains the same each time.

As with any problem involving a percentage, it is important that you start by identifying the 'whole' or 100% (see p.26).

You also need to be able to convert between percentages and decimals confidently (see p.25).

? Now try these...

1 Peter buys a house for £120 000. The estate agent tells him it will increase in value at a rate of 2% a year. How much will the house be worth after 10 years?

2 A car has 90 litres of petrol in its tank. Travelling at a constant speed of 60mph, the amount of fuel in the tank decreases by 5% an hour.
  a) How much petrol will be in the tank after 10 hours of travelling at this speed?
  b) Starting with a full tank of petrol (90 litres), for how many hours can the car travel at 60mph before it runs out of petrol?

✓ You should already know...

- **how to round numbers to the nearest 10, 100 and 1000**
- **how to estimate the answers to simple calculations**
- **how to check answers are reasonable by looking at the size of the numbers involved**
- **how to use your knowledge of maths to check results obtained using a calculator.**

ℹ You also need to know...

- **how to round numbers to a given number of decimal places**
- **how to round a number to a given number of significant figures.**

Numbers containing decimals can be rounded to a given number of **decimal places (d.p.)**. Decimal places are counted from the decimal point. For example, numbers with one decimal place have one digit after the decimal point, numbers with two decimal places have two digits after the decimal point etc.

To round a number in this way, you need to look at the digit that appears directly after the decimal place you are rounding to. If that digit is **5 or more** (i.e. 5, 6, 7, 8 or 9) you round up.

The same rule applies if you are rounding to a given number of **significant figures (s.f.)**.

The first significant figure in a number is the first digit that is not a zero. All the digits that come after this one are counted as significant figures even if they are zeros.

Examples

1 Round the following numbers to 3 d.p., 2 d.p. and 1 d.p.

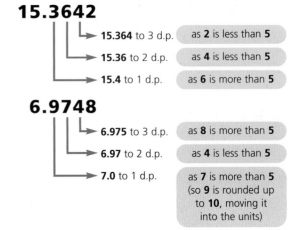

15.3642

- 15.364 to 3 d.p. — as **2** is less than **5**
- 15.36 to 2 d.p. — as **4** is less than **5**
- 15.4 to 1 d.p. — as **6** is more than **5**

6.9748

- 6.975 to 3 d.p. — as **8** is more than **5**
- 6.97 to 2 d.p. — as **4** is less than **5**
- 7.0 to 1 d.p. — as **7** is more than **5** (so **9** is rounded up to **10**, moving it into the units)

2 Round the following numbers to 3 s.f., 2 s.f. and 1 s.f.

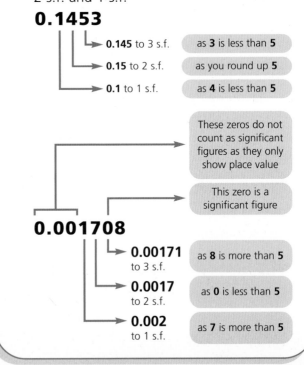

0.1453

- 0.145 to 3 s.f. — as **3** is less than **5**
- 0.15 to 2 s.f. — as you round up **5**
- 0.1 to 1 s.f. — as **4** is less than **5**

These zeros do not count as significant figures as they only show place value

This zero is a significant figure

0.001708

- 0.00171 to 3 s.f. — as **8** is more than **5**
- 0.0017 to 2 s.f. — as **0** is less than **5**
- 0.002 to 1 s.f. — as **7** is more than **5**

? Now try these...

1 Round these to the given number of decimal places:
- **a)** 5.37 to 1 d.p.
- **b)** 18.015 to 2 d.p. and 1 d.p.
- **c)** 37.519 to 2 d.p. and 1 d.p.
- **d)** 0.0749 to 3 d.p., 2 d.p. and 1 d.p.

2 Round these to the given number of significant figures:
- **a)** 0.1259 to 1 s.f., 2 s.f. and 3 s.f.
- **b)** 12.05 to 1 s.f., 2 s.f. and 3 s.f.
- **c)** 67 029 to 1 s.f., 2 s.f., 3 s.f. and 4 s.f.
- **d)** 0.0000185 to 1 s.f., 2 s.f. and 3 s.f.

Approximating & Checking

You need to know...

- **how to check your answers by applying inverse operations or estimating using approximations.**

You can check your answers to calculations in two ways.

The first method is to use approximation to check that your answer looks reasonable i.e. that it is about the size you would expect it to be, as shown on the facing page.

When performing calculations involving lots of numbers, you can make a quick estimate by rounding each value to 1 s.f. This will give you the 'order of magnitude' of your expected answer i.e. it will tell you whether your answer will be in the tens, hundreds, thousands, etc. or whether it will be a decimal.

If your answer seems reasonable, you can then go on to check it for accuracy. To do this, start with your answer and work backwards through the calculation using inverse operations i.e. reversing the maths. If your answer is correct, you should end up with the number you first started with.

Examples

1 What order of magnitude would you expect for the answer to this calculation?

$$\frac{152 \times 37}{8}$$

Round all the numbers involved to 1 s.f.

$$\frac{200 \times 40}{10} = \frac{80\,000}{10} = 800$$

So, the answer will be in the high hundreds! (The correct answer is 703).

2 Rachael goes shopping and buys the following items:

1 skirt at £6.99
2 tops at £3.75 each
1 pair of flip flops at £2.99

She pays with a £20 note and is given £1.52 change. Use estimation and inverse operations to check whether she has been given the correct change.

By estimation...
£20 − £7 − £4 − £4 − £3 = £2
She has received roughly the right amount of change.

Using inverse operations...
£1.52 + £2.99 + £3.75 + £3.75 + £6.99 = £19.00
She has been short-changed by £1.

Now try these...

1 What order of magnitude would you expect for the answer to each of these calculations?
  a) 29 x 11
  b) 69 + 78 − 50
  c) $\frac{1000}{250}$
  d) $\frac{47 \times 120}{96}$

2 Check the following calculations by estimation and then for accuracy.
  a) 13 + 29 + 43 = 82
  b) 9.06 + 11.58 + 7.23 + 13.86 = 41.73
  c) $\frac{31 - 182}{57} = 26.5$
  d) $\frac{31 + 182}{57} = 3.74$

You should already know...

- the different roles played by letter symbols in algebra
- the difference in meaning between the words equation, formula, identity and expression
- that the letter symbols in algebra obey the rules of arithmetic
- how to simplify expressions by collecting like terms.

You also need to know...

- how to simplify or transform an expression by multiplying out a single pair of brackets.

A number or letter immediately in front of brackets means that everything inside the brackets must be multiplied by that number or letter.

In algebra, when multiplying with negative and positive numbers and letters, the rules are the same as in arithmetic (see p.6)

$$+ \times + = +$$
$$- \times - = +$$
If the signs are the **same**, the answer is positive.

$$+ \times - = -$$
$$- \times + = -$$
If they are **different**, the answer is negative.

When you have multiplied out the brackets, you may need to **simplify** the expression by **collecting like terms**.

Examples

Multiply out the brackets and where possible simplify the following expressions.

1. $6(a + 1)$

   $= 6 \times a + 6 \times 1$
   $= 6a + 6$

   a and 1 must both be multiplied by 6

2. $8(2x + 4y - 3z)$

   $= 8 \times 2x + 8 \times 4y + 8 \times -3z$
   $= 16x + 32y - 24z$

3. $3(p + 2) + 2(p - 1)$

   $= 3 \times p + 3 \times 2 + 2 \times p + 2 \times -1$
   $= 3p + 6 + 2p - 2$
   $= 3p + 2p + 6 - 2$
   $= 5p + 4$

   Now simplify the expression by collecting like terms

4. $a(a + 3) + b(a - 4)$

   $= a \times a + a \times 3 + b \times a + b \times -4$
   $= a^2 + 3a + ab - 4b$

   Remember, $a \times a = a^2$

5. $4(x + 3) + y(z - 5)$

   $= 4 \times x + 4 \times 3 + y \times z + y \times -5$
   $= 4x + 12 + yz - 5y$

6. $3p(p + 6) + 4p(2p + 1)$

   $= 3p \times p + 3p \times 6 + 4p \times 2p + 4p \times 1$
   $= 3p^2 + 18p + 8p^2 + 4p$
   $= 11p^2 + 22p$

? Now try these...

Multiply out the brackets and, where possible, simplify the following expressions:

1. $5(p + 4)$
2. $6(2x - 3)$
3. $x(x + y + 3)$
4. $a(a + b)$
5. $5(3 - 2x + 7)$
6. $5(2 - 3x) + 7$
7. $11(5 - 3x) - 9$
8. $10(3x - 4) - 9$
9. $3x(2x + 5y - 9)$
10. $3(x + 2) + 2(x - 1)$
11. $a(2a + b) + b(2b + a)$
12. $2(a + b) + a(2b + c) + 2b(a + c)$
13. $6(a + b + c) + 2(2a - 2b - 2c)$
14. $2p(p - 3) + 3p(2p - 2)$
15. $5a(b + 2) - 3a(b - 2)$

Basic Algebra

ℹ **You need to know...**

- **how to expand the product of two linear expressions**
- **how to square a linear expression**
- **how to factorise expressions by taking out common factors.**

A **linear expression** is one that has no powers higher than 1, e.g. $3a - 7$. The **product** of two linear expressions is found by multiplying them together, e.g. $(3a - 7)(2a + 2)$. Each term from the first bracket must be multiplied by each term from the second bracket. The expression can then be **simplified** by **collecting like terms**. This process is called **expansion**.

When an expression is **squared** it is multiplied by itself. It can be expanded in the same way by writing the expression out twice, e.g. $(3a + 5)^2$ becomes $(3a + 5)(3a + 5)$.

Factorising is the opposite of expansion and therefore means putting brackets in. To factorise an expression you need to find the common factors of all the terms...

1. Identify the largest number that divides into all the terms.
2. Identify which letters appear in all the terms and for each letter find the highest common power.
3. Write down these common factors and open brackets.
4. Inside the brackets write all the values that you need to multiply the common factors by to result in the original expression.
5. Check your answer by expanding the expression.

Examples

1. Multiply out the following expression:

$$(3a - 7)(2a + 2)$$

$$= 3a \times 2a + 3a \times 2 + \text{-}7 \times 2a + \text{-}7 \times 2$$
$$= 6a^2 + 6a - 14a - 14 \quad \text{remember, } a \times a = a^2$$
$$= 6a^2 - 8a - 14$$

2. Expand the following linear expression:
$$(2x + 6)^2$$

$$= (2x + 6)(2x + 6)$$
$$= 2x \times 2x + 2x \times 6 + 6 \times 2x + 6 \times 6$$
$$= 4x^2 + 12x + 12x + 36$$
$$= 4x^2 + 24x + 36$$

3. Factorise the following expression:
$$10a^3b - 20a^2b^2 + 30a^2c$$

10 — the highest common factor of 10, 20 and 30 is 10

10a — a is the only letter to appear in all the terms

10a² — ...and a^2 is its highest power in all the terms – remember, $a^3 = a^2 \times a$

$$= 10a^2(ab - 2b^2 + 3c)$$

$10a^2 \times ab = 10a^3b$
$10a^2 \times \text{-}2b^2 = \text{-}20a^2b^2$
$10a^2 \times 3c = 30a^2c$

❓ **Now try these...**

1. Expand and simplify these expressions:
   a) $(2x - 4)(3x + 6)$
   b) $(2x + 7)^2$
   c) $(2a + b)(5a + 3b)$
   d) $(a - b)^2$

2. Factorise these expressions:
   a) $2x^2 - 8$
   b) $5ab - 10bc$
   c) $9x^2y - 6xz - 3xyz$
   d) $4p^3 + 6p^2 + 12p^2q$

✓ You should already know...

- **how to solve simple equations by balancing both sides.**

ⓘ You also need to know...

- **how to solve linear equations using inverse operations**
- **how to solve equations using trial and improvement.**

To solve an equation, collect all the letters on one side and all the numbers on the other. Then, reduce it to a single letter and number e.g. $x = 6$. To do this, you need to use **inverse operations** (inverse means opposite):

$+$ and $-$ are inverse operations

$\times$ and $\div$ are inverse operations

Inverse operations can be used to cancel out unwanted numbers, but you must always remember to keep the equation balanced. For example, if you add a number to one side, you must add it to the other side too.

You can check your answer by putting it into the original equation, replacing the letter term.

Trial and improvement is a method used to find an approximate solution to an equation. Start by estimating a solution. Try your estimate out by putting it into the equation, replacing the letter term – it will probably be too big or too small. Use the results of your first trial to make a second estimate, better than the first. Each estimate you try should be better than the last, bringing you closer to the solution. Keep going until you get an answer accurate enough for your purposes.

Examples

① Solve the equation $x - 4 = 20$.

$$x - 4 = 20$$
$$x - 4 + 4 = 20 + 4$$
$$x = 24$$

> Add **4** to both sides to leave x on its own (**-4 + 4 = 0**)

> Now, do the maths to find the solution

> Check your answer **24 − 4 = 20**

② Solve the equation $4(x - 2) = 20$.

$$4(x - 2) = 20$$
$$4x - 8 = 20$$
$$4x - 8 + 8 = 20 + 8$$
$$4x = 28$$
$$\frac{4x}{4} = \frac{28}{4}$$
$$x = 7$$

> Multiply out brackets first

> Get the letter term on its own

> Reduce to a single letter and number

> **÷4** is the inverse operation of **×4**

> Check your answer: **4(7 − 2) = 20**

③ Use trial and improvement to solve the equation $x^2 = 18$ (to 2 decimal places).

First estimate: **4**
$4^2 = 16$ — Too small

Second estimate: **5**
$5^2 = 25$ — Too big

The value of x must lie between 4 and 5, so…

Third estimate: **4.5**
$4.5^2 = 20.25$ — Too big

Keep improving your estimates until you get an answer that is close enough:

$4.2^2 = 17.64$ — Too small
$4.3^2 = 18.49$ — Too big
$4.25^2 = 18.0625$ — Too big
$4.24^2 = 17.9776$ — Closest

So, $x = 4.24$ (2 d.p.)

? Now try these...

① Solve these equations:

a) $2p - 3 = 5$

b) $5(x + 6) = 80$

c) $2(x - 4) + 3 = 23$

d) $a + 5 = 3a - 3$

② Use trial and improvement to solve these equations to 1 d.p.:

a) $x^2 = 29$

b) $x^2 = 109$

c) $x^2 = 78$

d) $x^2 = 7$

Algebraic Equations

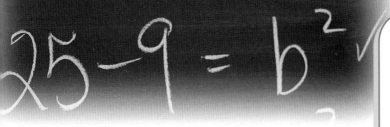

i You need to know...

- **how to solve simultaneous linear equations using algebraic methods.**

Simultaneous equations can be formed when you have a pair of related equations, each containing the same two unknown values (e.g. x and y). Solving simultaneous equations involves working with both equations at the same time to find a pair of values that works for both of them.

To solve simultaneous equations, start by combining the two equations to eliminate either x or y. It might be possible to substitute one equation directly into the other. If not, you need to add or subtract the two equations. To do this, both equations need to contain the same number of x's or y's so it may be necessary to multiply one or both of the equations first.

The resulting linear equation can be solved to find the value of one of the unknowns. This value is then substituted into one of the original equations to find the other unknown. Check your solution by substituting both values into the remaining original equation.

Alternatively, simultaneous equations can be solved by drawing graphs (see p.58).

Examples

Solve the simultaneous equations to find values for x and y.

1 $5x + y = 49$ **(1)**
$y = 2x$ **(2)**

$5x + 2x = 49$
$7x = 49$
$x = 7$

> Substitute equation **(2)** directly into equation **(1)**, then solve in the usual way.

$y = 2 \times 7$
$y = 14$

> Then substitute the x value into equation **(2)** to find y.

> Check: $5x + y = 49$
> $5 \times 7 + 14 = 49$

2 $2x + y = 8$ **(1)**
$x + y = 5$ **(2)**
$x = 3$

> Here, subtracting equation **(2)** from equation **(1)** immediately eliminates the y terms.

$(2 \times 3) + y = 8$
$6 + y = 8$
$y = 8 - 6$
$y = 2$

> Then substitute into equation **(1)**

> Check: $x + y = 5$
> $3 + 2 = 5$

3 $2x + y = 17$ **(1)**
$3x + 2y = 28$ **(2)**

$4x + 2y = 34$ **(1)**
$3x + 2y = 28$ **(2)**
$x = 6$

> Multiply equation **(1)** by 2 so there are the same number of y's in both equations

> Solve by subtracting **(2)** from **(1)** as before

$2 \times 6 + y = 17$
$12 + y = 17$
$y = 17 - 12$
$y = 5$

> Check: $3x + 2y = 28$
> $3 \times 6 + 2 \times 5 = 28$

? Now try these...

Solve these pairs of equations:

1 $x + 2y = 10$
$x = 3y$

2 $5a + b = 14$
$3a + b = 10$

3 $6x + 2y = 19$
$x - 2y = 2$

4 $2p + q = 7$
$3p + 2q = 11$

5 $2x - 5y = 1$
$5x + 3y = 18$

✓ You should already know...

- **how to use algebra to solve simple problems**

ⓘ You also need to know...

- **how to form and solve linear equations.**

Providing you are given enough information, forming a linear equation can help you to find all sorts of unknown values e.g. missing angles and side lengths in shapes. In addition to the information you are given in the question you may also need to draw upon your own knowledge of maths.

For example, you could be given the sizes of two angles in a triangle and asked to find the missing one. To answer the question you need to know that the interior angles of a triangle always add up to 180° (see p.70).

? Now try these...

1. The angles of a triangle are d°, 2d° and 3d°. What is the size of each angle?

2. I think of a number. I add 9 to the number then divide the total by 3. The answer is 4. What was my number?

3. Karen is 6 years older than her brother. Their ages added together make 28. How old is Karen?

4. My garden is 5 metres narrower than my next-door neighbour's garden. Both gardens together are 45 metres wide. How wide is my garden?

5. Dan's mother is exactly three times older than Dan. The difference between their ages is 24 years. How old is Dan's mother?

Examples

1. John's dad weighs twice as much as John. Their combined weight is 153kg. How much does John's dad weigh?

If John's weight is **j**, his dad's weight is **2j**. Their combined weight is 153kg:

$$j + 2j = 153$$
$$3j = 153$$
$$j = \frac{153}{3}$$

This is John's weight $$j = 51kg$$

Remember, the question asks 'How much does John's dad weigh?'

$$\text{John's dad} = 2j$$
$$= 2 \times 51kg$$
$$= 102kg$$

2. In this rectangle, the length is three times the width. The perimeter of the rectangle is 24cm. Find the length of the rectangle.

It might help if you draw and label a rectangle.

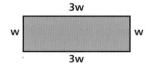

The perimeter (**P**) of a rectangle is found by adding all the sides together.

If w = width, then length = 3w	$P = w + 3w + w + 3w$
	$P = 8w$
We know P = 24 so solve the equation	$8w = 24cm$
	$w = 3cm$
If w = 3 then...	length = 3w
	length = 3 × 3cm
	length = 9cm
Then check $3 + 9 + 3 + 9 = 24$	
Write the answer	**The length is 9cm**

Solving Problems

ℹ You need to know...

- **how to form linear equations to help solve mathematical problems.**

Word problems can be quite complicated. It is important to read the question carefully before you start. Pick out the important mathematical bits of the question, then break it down into simple stages and decide how to deal with it bit by bit. Always remember to check your answer when you have finished. Just asking yourself whether the answer is sensible can sometimes be enough to spot a mistake.

? Now try these...

1. The sides of a triangle are $(3x + 4)$cm, $(2x - 1)$cm and $(3x + 3)$cm. The perimeter of the triangle is 26cm. Find the lengths of the sides.
2. Tony is 11 years younger than Ken. Sue is 5 years younger than Tony. Their combined age is the same as 6 times Sue's age. How old are Ken, Tony and Sue?
3. Raj took four letters to the Post Office. The second letter was 25g heavier than the first, the third letter was 18g lighter than the first and the fourth letter was double the weight of the second. The combined weight of the four letters was 13g less than four times the weight of the second letter. What did the letters weigh?

Examples

1. I think of a number. If I take away 1 and multiply the result by 4, the answer is the same as I get when I multiply the number by 2 and add 4 to the result. What is my number?

    Let the number be **n**.
    First part = 4(n − 1)
    Second part = 2n + 4
    The two expressions are equal so:
    4(n − 1) = 2n + 4
    4n − 4 = 2n + 4
    4n − 4̶ + 4̶ = 2n + 4 + 4
    4n = 2n + 8
    4n − 2n = 2̶n̶ + 8 − 2̶n̶
    2n = 8
    n = 4

    The number is 4.

    > Check: (4 − 1) x 4 = 12 and (2 x 4) + 4 = 12

2. A rectangle has a length of $(2p + 3)$cm and a width of $(3p − 1)$cm. Its perimeter is 54cm. What is the area of the rectangle?
    Area is found by multiplying length by width. By solving an equation involving length, width and perimeter we can find the length and width which means we can then find the area.

    2(2p + 3) + 2(3p − 1) = 54
    4p + 6 + 6p − 2 = 54
    10p + 4 = 54
    10p + 4̶ − 4̶ = 54 − 4
    10p = 50
    p = 5

    Length = 2 x 5 + 3 = 13cm Substitute the value for p into the
    Width = 3 x 5 − 1 = 14cm expressions for
    Area = 13 x 14 = 182cm² length and width

    > Check: 2 x 13 + 2 x 14 = 54

✓ You should already know...

- **how to construct simple formulae expressed in words and algebraic form.**

ℹ You also need to know...

- **how to construct and use algebraic formulae.**

To construct a formula using algebra you first need to pick out the mathematical bits of the question. Once you know how the formula is to be used, you can start to put it together.

1. Write down the letters you will use for each **variable** – it helps to use obvious ones, like **C** for cost.
2. Write down the letter you are using for the **final answer or total**, followed by an equals sign.
3. Use the information from the question to build your formula – what maths do you need to use?
4. Make sure all the values used in the formula are in the **same units**, for example, you cannot have both **£** and **p** in the same formula.
5. When you have written the formula, check that the algebra you have used is correct, e.g. **0.2d** not **d0.2**.

To use a formula, you need to substitute (see p.46) the appropriate values into the equation and solve it.

Examples

① A taxi company makes a fixed charge of £2.40 per journey plus 20p per kilometre.

a) Write a formula for the total cost of the journey.

> Let **C** stand for the total cost and **d** stand for the distance in kilometres.

C = 0.2d + 2.40

> This is the price per km (20p = £0.20) x distance travelled + fixed charge

b) What is the cost of a journey of 5km?

C = 0.2d + 2.40 when **d = 5km**
C = (0.2 x 5) + 2.40
C = 1 + 2.40 = **£3.40**

② Books bought from an internet company cost £4.99 each. The delivery charge is an extra £2.99 per order.

a) Write a formula for the total cost of an order.

> Let **C** stand for the total cost and **b** stand for the number of books ordered.

C = 4.99b + 2.99

b) What is the total cost of 10 books?

if **b = 10**...
C = (4.99 x 10) + 2.99
C = 49.90 + 2.99
C = **£52.89**

? Now try these...

① At the cinema, an adult ticket costs £7 and a child ticket costs £2.50.
   a) Write a formula for the cost of a group visit to the cinema.
   b) What will be the cost of a cinema trip for 6 adults and 2 children?

② Kevin is a salesperson. For every journey, he can claim a fixed amount of £10 for meals plus 40p per mile for travel expenses.
   a) Write a formula for the total amount of expenses claimed for every journey.
   b) How much can Kevin claim for a journey of 120 miles?

Formulae

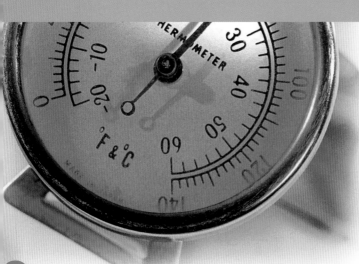

You need to know...

- **how to change the subject of a formula.**

A formula will usually have several different variables that change their values according to the circumstances. It is possible to rearrange a formula (also called **changing the subject**), so that it can be used to find any one of the variables.

Changing the subject of the formula uses very similar rules to those used in solving equations. A formula always has an equals sign, so it must always be balanced – whatever you do to one side of the formula must also be done to the other side.

Go through these steps in order, but remember they won't all apply to every formula…

1. deal with square roots first by squaring each side
2. get rid of any fractions by multiplying each side by the denominator
3. use +, −, x, ÷ and $\sqrt{}$ to move the rest of the terms until the new subject is left on its own.

Examples

1. $C = \pi d$ is the formula for the circumference of a circle, where d is the diameter. Rearrange the formula to make d the subject.

$$C = \pi d$$
$$\frac{C}{\pi} = \frac{\pi d}{\pi}$$
$$\frac{C}{\pi} = d$$

so $d = \dfrac{C}{\pi}$

2. The formula for changing temperature in °F to °C is:

$$C = \frac{5(F - 32)}{9}$$

Make F the subject of the formula.

$$C = \frac{5(F - 32)}{9}$$
$$C \times 9 = \frac{5(F - 32)}{9} \times 9$$
$$9C = 5(F - 32)$$
$$\frac{9C}{5} = \frac{5(F - 32)}{5}$$
$$\frac{9C}{5} = F - 32$$
$$\frac{9C}{5} + 32 = F - 32 + 32$$
$$\frac{9C}{5} + 32 = F$$

so $F = \dfrac{9C}{5} + 32$

Now try these...

Make the letter in brackets the subject of the formula:

1. $a = b - c$ (b)
2. $z = x + y$ (y)
3. $p = q + 10s$ (q)
4. $v = \dfrac{w}{100}$ (w)

5. $V = \dfrac{2R}{l}$ (R)
6. $V = \dfrac{2R}{l}$ (l)
7. $x = y^2 + z$ (y)
8. $A = LW$ (W)
9. $a = \sqrt{2b} - c$ (b)
10. $a = \sqrt{2b} - c$ (c)

ⓘ You need to know...

- **how to find the value of an expression or formula by substituting.**

There are two particular mathematical topics where you will be expected to find a value by substituting: using a formula and making a table of values for a linear graph.

A **formula** usually relates to a real life situation that involves mathematical rules. You may be given a special formula, such as the one for changing between Fahrenheit and Celsius, and be asked to use it.

When you are drawing the graph of an equation (see p.54), it helps to begin by making a **table of values**. This makes it easier to see the pairs of coordinates that are needed to plot the graph. You may need to choose values of x, and then substitute them into the equation to work out the corresponding values of y.

Examples

① The formula to change a temperature from degrees Celsius (°C) to degrees Fahrenheit (°F) is:

$$F = \frac{9C}{5} + 32$$

Find the value of 16°C in °F.

$$F = \frac{9C}{5} + 32$$

$$= \frac{9 \times 16}{5} + 32$$

$$= \frac{144}{5} + 32$$

$$= 28.8 + 32 = 60.8°F$$

② The cost of hiring a dinghy is £4 per hour plus a fixed charge of £5. Write a formula for the total cost of hiring a dinghy, and use the formula to find the cost of hiring it for 3 hours.

C = 4h + 5
When h = 3...
C = 4 x 3 + 5
C = 12 + 5 = £17

> Let **C** stand for cost and **h** stand for number of hours.

③ Complete the table of values for
y = 4x – 5

x	-2	-1	0
y = 4x – 5			

When x = -2,
y = 4x – 5 = (4 x -2) – 5 = -8 – 5 = -13
When x = -1,
y = 4x – 5 = (4 x -1) – 5 = -4 – 5 = -9
When x = 0,
y = 4x – 5 = (4 x 0) – 5 = 0 – 5 = -5

x	-2	-1	0
y = 4x – 5	-13	-9	-5

? Now try these...

① Use the formula in Example 1 to change 23°C to °F.
② The recommended time to cook turkey is 35 minutes per kilogram plus an extra 20 minutes. Write a formula for the time to cook a turkey and use it to find the time to cook a 5kg turkey.
③ In science, Satvinder is using the formula v = u + at. In one experiment she finds that u = 30, a = -3 and t = 6. Use the formula to calculate v.
④ Complete this table of values for the equation y = 3x + 9.

x	-2	-1	0	1	2
y = 3x + 9					

Substitution

i You need to know...

- **how to evaluate a formula.**

Formulae are commonly used in maths and science. To **evaluate** a formula you need to work out its value using the given **variables**. Substituting variables is not difficult, but take care when evaluating formulae involving negative numbers and powers.

Remember that in algebra, the same rules apply as in arithmetic...

BIDMAS

Brackets

Indices (or powers)

Divisions and **M**ultiplications (in any order)

Additions and **S**ubtractions (in any order)

? Now try these...

1. Use the formula in Example 1 to find the volume of a sphere with a radius of 12cm.

2. Rearrange the formula in Example 1 to make r the subject of the formula. Use your formula to find the radius of a sphere with a volume of 600cm³.

3. Use the formula in Example 2 to find the length of the diagonal of a rectangle with length 9cm and width 2.5cm.

4. Rearrange the formula in Example 2 to make b the subject. Use your formula to find the length of a rectangle with width 6cm and diagonal length 10cm.

5. Use the formula in Example 3 to find the amount of interest charged on a loan of £8000 at 3.9% for 3 years.

6. Rearrange the formula in Example 3 to make R the subject of the formula. Use your formula to find the percentage interest rate needed to give interest of £120 on a loan of £2000 for 4 years.

Examples

1. The formula for the volume of a sphere is $\frac{4}{3}\pi r^3$ where r is the radius of the sphere. Find the volume of a sphere with a radius of 5cm.

$$V = \frac{4}{3}\pi 5^3$$

$$V = \frac{4}{3} \times 3.14 \times 125 \quad \text{Deal with the cube first}$$

$$V = \frac{4}{3} \times 392.5 \quad \text{Then calculate the fraction}$$

$$V = 523.3\text{cm}^3$$

2. The length (ℓ) of the diagonal of a rectangle is given by the formula $\ell = \sqrt{a^2 + b^2}$ where a is the width and b is the length. Find the length of the diagonal of a rectangle with length 4cm and width 3cm.

$$\ell = \sqrt{3^2 + 4^2} \quad \text{Deal with the indices first}$$
$$\ell = \sqrt{9 + 16}$$
$$\ell = \sqrt{25} \quad \text{Then the square root}$$
$$\ell = 5\text{cm}$$

3. The formula used by a bank to work out the amount of interest (£) to charge on a loan is $I = \frac{PRT}{100}$ when P is the principal (original amount borrowed), R is the interest rate (%) and T is the number of years of the loan. Find the interest due on a loan of £5000 at 4.2% for 5 years.

$$I = \frac{5000 \times 4.2 \times 5}{100}$$

$$I = \frac{105\,000}{100}$$

$$I = £1050$$

✓ You should already know...

- **that a number pattern is a sequence of numbers that are connected by a rule**
- **how to recognise and describe simple number patterns.**

ⓘ You also need to know...

- **how to recognise and describe sequences**
- **how to continue a sequence using a rule.**

You should already know how to find the rule for a number pattern by looking at the difference between the terms.

Once you know the rule for a sequence, you can use it to continue the sequence in either direction. You can also fill in any missing terms in the sequence.

To write down a sequence using a rule...

1. write down the first term
2. use the rule to generate the next term
3. continue to use the rule until you have the correct number of terms.

To fill in missing terms in a sequence...

1. write down the sequence, including the spaces for missing terms
2. use the given terms to find the rule for the sequence (remember, if you work backwards through the sequence, you need to use the opposite operation)
3. use the rule to find the missing terms.

Examples

1. The 1st term of a sequence is 8 and the rule is 'subtract 1 from the previous term'. Write down the first five terms:

   8 − 1 = 7, 7 − 1 = 6, 6 − 1 = 5, 5 − 1 = 4
   The sequence is: 8, 7, 6, 5, 4

2. The 1st term of a sequence is 2 and the rule is 'multiply the previous term by 6'. Write down the first four terms:

   2 x 6 = 12, 12 x 6 = 72, 72 x 6 = 432
   The sequence is: 2, 12, 72, 432

3. Find the missing terms in this sequence:
   2, ___ , 12, 17, ___

   The difference between **12** and **17** is **5**.
   2 + 5 = 7 and **12 − 5 = 7** so the rule must be 'add 5 to the previous term'.
   The sequence is: 2, 7, 12, 17, 22

4. Find the missing terms in this sequence:
   ___ , 6, ___ , 24, 48

   The terms are increasing in value so the rule must be add or multiply.
   24 + 24 = 48, so the rule is either 'add 24', or 'x 2'. **6 + 24 = 30**, but **24 − 24 = 0** so the rule must be 'multiply the previous term by 2'. To find the first term, work backwards from 6, using the opposite of 'x 2' which is '÷ 2'. So **6 ÷ 2 = 3**.
   The sequence is: 3, 6, 12, 24, 48

? Now try these...

1. Write down the first five terms of each sequence:
   a) The first term is 75, the rule is 'subtract 8 from the previous term'.
   b) The first term is 1, the rule is 'multiply the previous term by 7'.

2. Find the missing terms in each sequence:
   a) 1, 5, ___, ___, 15
   b) ___ , 6, 18, ___, 162
   c) ___ , 400, ___ , 4, 0.4
   d) 180, ___ , ___ , 120, ___

Number Patterns

i You need to know...

- **how to recognise and describe common sequences.**

There are some special sequences of numbers that you need to know and recognise. The two obvious sequences are the odd and even numbers, which are both generated by the rule 'add 2 to the previous term'. You should also be familiar with **square numbers**, **triangle numbers** and **cube numbers**. All three of these sequences are easy to describe using diagrams, which help to explain the rule.

You will need to learn...
1. at least the first ten square numbers
2. at least the first five cube numbers
3. at least the first five triangle numbers.

Examples

1 What are the first four square numbers?

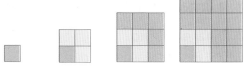

1   **4**   **9**   **16**

($1^2 = 1\times1$) ($2^2 = 2\times2$) ($3^2 = 3\times3$) ($4^2 = 4\times4$)

> Square numbers are generated in the same way as finding the area of a square.

The 1st square number is 1 x 1 = 1, so the 10th square number is 10 x 10 = 100.

2 What are the first four cube numbers?

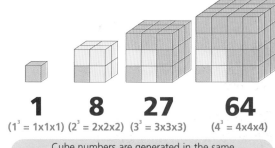

1   **8**   **27**   **64**

($1^3 = 1\times1\times1$) ($2^3 = 2\times2\times2$) ($3^3 = 3\times3\times3$) ($4^3 = 4\times4\times4$)

> Cube numbers are generated in the same way as finding the volume of a cube.

The 1st cube number is 1 x 1 x 1 = 1, so the 10th cube number is 10 x 10 x 10 = 1000.

3 What are the first four triangle numbers?

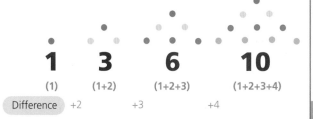

1   **3**   **6**   **10**

(1)   (1+2)   (1+2+3)   (1+2+3+4)

Difference +2   +3   +4

> Triangle numbers are the number of dots needed to make triangles. Each triangle is made by adding a new base, which is one dot bigger than the previous one. The difference between terms increases by 1 every time.

Each term is found by adding the consecutive integers up to and including the number of that term, e.g.
4th term = 1 + 2 + 3 + 4 = 10.

? Now try these...

1. Write down the first ten square numbers.
2. What is the 12th square number?
3. Write down the first ten cube numbers.
4. What is the 12th cube number?
5. Draw diagrams for the first eight triangle numbers.
6. Write down the first eight triangle numbers.
7. Without drawing a diagram, what is the 9th triangle number?

- **how to find and describe the nth term of a linear sequence.**

A **linear sequence** is a number sequence in which the terms increase or decrease by the same amount each time i.e. they follow a simple add or subtract rule.

A formula can be used to calculate the value of any term in a linear sequence. In this formula **n** is used to represent the position of the term in the sequence (1st, 2nd, 3rd etc.) so this method is called finding the **nth term**. The formula takes the form: **nth term = an + b**

To use the formula…

1. Number each term in the sequence. These numbers are values for **n**.
2. Find the difference between the terms in the sequence. If the numbers in the sequence increase, it will be a positive number. If the numbers decrease, it will be a negative number. This number is your value for **a**.
3. Calculate the value of **an** (a x n) for each given term in the sequence and write your answer directly beneath that term.
4. Now subtract the bottom number (your value for an) from the top number (the term). Write down your answer, including the + or − sign. The answer should be the same for each term. This is your value for **b**.
5. Substitute your values for a and b into the formula **nth term = an + b**.
6. To find the value of a specific term in the sequence, substitute the number of the term for n in the formula.

Example

Here is a sequence: **7 11 15 19 23**

a) Find a formula for the nth term of the sequence.

Number the terms. These numbers are values for **n**.	1	2	3	4	5
	7	**11**	**15**	**19**	**23**

The difference between each term is **+4**. This is your value for **a**.

+4   +4   +4   +4

So, the formula starts with **4n**. Calculate **4n** for each term.

4   8   12   16   20

Subtract these numbers from the original sequence to find the value for **b**, e.g. **7 - 4 = +3**

+3   +3   +3   +3   +3

The formula for the nth term is **4n + 3**

b) What will be the 100th term in the sequence?

nth term = 4n + 3

    = 4 x 100 + 3   *Substitute 100 for the n in the formula*

    = 400 + 3 = **403**

c) The number 111 is in the sequence, which term is it?

$$4n + 3 = \text{nth term}$$
$$4n + 3 = 111$$ *If 111 is in the sequence, then...*
$$4n + \cancel{3} - \cancel{3} = 111 - 3$$ *Solve the equation*
$$4n = 108$$
$$\frac{\cancel{4}n}{\cancel{4}} = \frac{108}{4}$$
$$n = 27$$

So 111 is the **27th term**.

For each of these sequences…

a) find the nth term

b) use the formula to find the 50th term.

1. 5, 8, 11, 14, 17
2. -27, -25, -23, -21, -19
3. 1, 1.5, 2, 2.5, 3
4. In question 3 the number 25.5 appears later in the sequence. Which term is it?

Number Patterns

ℹ You need to know...

- **how to find and use an expression for the nth term of a quadratic sequence.**

If the terms in a sequence increase or decrease by different amounts each time, it will not produce a straightforward, linear rule. It is possible, however, that this sort of sequence will produce a quadratic expression, i.e. an expression with n^2 in it. This method of finding the nth term involves finding differences. It is quite complex so make sure you label each line of sequences and differences so you don't get confused. For example, take the sequence 1, 9, 21, 37, 57...

1 Write down the original sequence and write the term numbers (n) above.	Term number (n): Original sequence:	1 2 3 4 5 **1 9 21 37 57**
2 Find the difference between the terms of the sequence (include +/-).	1st difference:	+8 +12 +16 +20
3 Find the difference between the 1st difference terms (include +/-).	2nd difference:	+4 +4 +4
4 If the second difference is constant the formula is quadratic so divide the second difference by 2. This is the number that goes in front of the **n²** in your formula...	$\dfrac{\text{2nd difference}}{2}$	$= \dfrac{4}{2} = 2$ **2n²...**
5 Work out $\dfrac{\text{2nd difference}}{2}$ **x n²** for each term to create a second sequence.	Term number (n): 2nd Sequence (2n²) =	1 2 3 4 5 **2 8 18 32 50**
6 Subtract each term of the 2nd sequence from the corresponding term in the original sequence...	Original Sequence – 2nd Sequence =	**-1 +1 +3 +5 +7**
7 Find the difference between the terms in this new sequence. This value goes in front of n to form the second part of the expression.	New difference:	+2 +2 +2 +2 **...+2n...**
8 Work out **new difference x n**.	Term number (n): 2n =	1 2 3 4 5 **2 4 6 8 10**
9 Subtract the first term of this sequence from the first term of the sequence in step **6**. This forms the last part of the expression (include +/–).	Step **6** – Step **8**:	-1 – 2 = -3 **...-3**
10 Write down the complete formula.	Formula:	**nth term = 2n² + 2n – 3**
To find a value of a term, simply substitute the term number for all the 'n's in the expression.	e.g. the 10th term	10th term $= 2 \times 10^2 + 2 \times 10 - 3$ $= 200 + 20 - 3 = \mathbf{217}$

❓ Now try these...

For each of these sequences, find an expression for the nth term and use it to find the 10th term in the sequence.

1. 0, 10, 26, 48, 76...
2. 3, 7, 13, 21, 31...
3. 5, 18, 41, 74, 117...
4. 8, 19, 34, 53, 76...
5. 2, 3, 6, 11, 18...

✓ You should already know...

- **that you can plot points on an axes using two coordinates (x,y).**

ℹ You also need to know...

- **how to use and understand coordinates in all four quadrants.**

When the x and y axes of a graph are extended beyond the origin, the axes of the graph divide the space into four parts. These parts are called **quadrants**. Each quadrant has different properties, which are shown in the coordinates of the point.

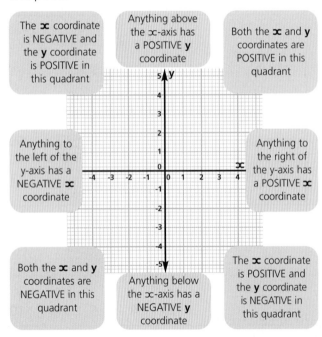

The x coordinate is NEGATIVE and the y coordinate is POSITIVE in this quadrant

Anything above the x-axis has a POSITIVE y coordinate

Both the x and y coordinates are POSITIVE in this quadrant

Anything to the left of the y-axis has a NEGATIVE x coordinate

Anything to the right of the y-axis has a POSITIVE x coordinate

Both the x and y coordinates are NEGATIVE in this quadrant

Anything below the x-axis has a NEGATIVE y coordinate

The x coordinate is POSITIVE and the y coordinate is NEGATIVE in this quadrant

To read and plot coordinates on a graph like this, follow the same rules as with all coordinates, i.e. x first (left or right from the origin), then y (up or down).

Example

Write down the coordinates of the points marked on the graph.

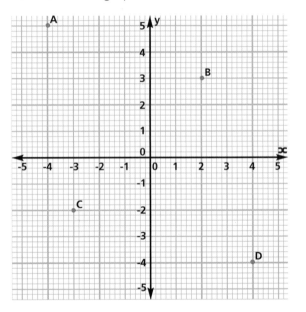

a) A (-4,5)   b) B (2,3)   c) C (-3,-2)   d) D (4,-4)

? Now try these...

1 On squared paper, draw and label x and y axes from −10 to 10.

    a) On your graph, plot and label these points:

      A (3,10), B (-7,-4), C (6,-6), and D (-2,3).

      Join points A and B with a straight line.

    b) What do you notice about point D?

2 Write down the coordinates of all the points marked on the graph alongside.

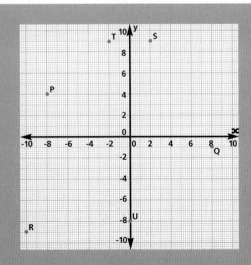

Graphs

ⓘ You need to know...

- **the general features of straight line graphs.**

There are three types of straight line graph that you need to recognise and be able to sketch if necessary:

1 vertical lines

2 horizontal lines

3 the main diagonal lines.

The lines are easy to recognise by their equations. Equations in the form **x = a number** give **vertical** line graphs. The line will cross the x-axis at 'the number', and will never cross the y-axis.

Equations in the form **y = a number** give **horizontal** line graphs. The line will cross the y-axis at 'the number', and will never cross the x-axis.

There are two main **diagonal** lines, the graph of **y = x** goes **up** from left to right, and **y = -x** goes **down** from left to right.

When you are asked to sketch the graph of an equation, remember that it will not be an accurately plotted graph, but the lines must be in reasonable or sensible positions on the axes.

❓ Now try these...

1 On squared paper, draw unnumbered x and y axes. Sketch and label the graphs of...

a) y = 4

b) x = -2

c) y = x

d) x = 8

e) y = -x

f) x = -6

2 Label any points where your lines cross the x or y axes and write down their coordinates.

Examples

For each question draw separate axes and draw the graphs of the following lines...

1 **a)** x = 3

b) x = -1

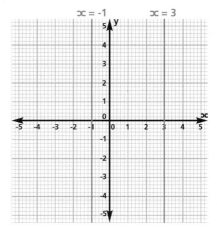

2 **a)** y = 5

b) y = -4

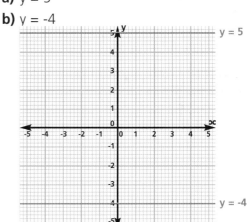

3 **a)** y = x

b) y = -x

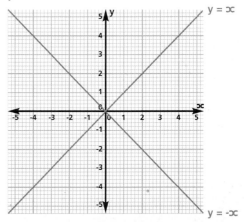

You need to know...

- **how to use coordinates to plot the graphs of linear equations.**

If an equation is linear, i.e. there are no x^2 terms or other powers of x, the graph of the equation will be a straight line.

Before you can draw an accurate graph of an equation, you need to produce a table of values. To do this, you will be given values of x from which to work out the values of y. Write down the equation and then substitute each given value of x from the table into the equation to find the corresponding y values (see p.46). Write the values of y into the correct positions in the table.

The table of values will provide pairs of x and y values that make up coordinates. Accurately plot each pair of coordinates on the graph, marking them with a cross or small dot. When all the points have been plotted, join them carefully with a ruler to form the graph – a straight line graph MUST be drawn with a ruler. When you join the points it will be obvious if any of them do not fit the straight line. If this occurs, these points must be wrong, so check your working and make sure that you have plotted each point correctly.

Example

Draw a table of values of x from -2 to 2 and use it to draw the graph of $y = 2x + 3$.

Substitute the values of x into the formula:

When $x = -2$, $y = 2 \times -2 + 3 = $ **-1**
When $x = -1$, $y = 2 \times -1 + 3 = $ **1**
When $x = 0$, $y = 2 \times 0 + 3 = $ **3**
When $x = 1$, $y = 2 \times 1 + 3 = $ **5**
When $x = 2$, $y = 2 \times 2 + 3 = $ **7**

x	-2	-1	0	1	2
y	-1	1	3	5	7

Now draw and label the graph using each pair of values as coordinates for the points.

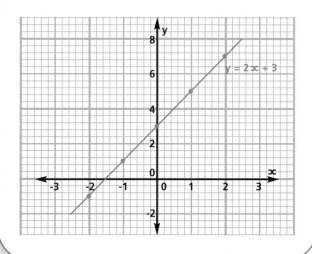

? Now try these...

1. Complete this table of values and use it to draw the graph of $y = 3x - 4$

x	-1	0	1	2	3
y					

2. Use values of x from -2 to 2 to make a table of values for the equation $y = \frac{1}{2}x + 5$. Use your table of values to plot the graph of $y = \frac{1}{2}x + 5$.

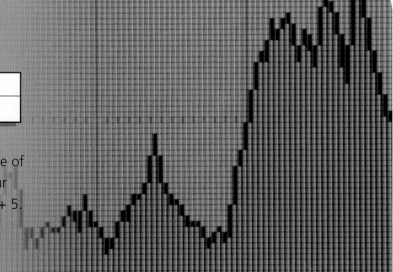

Graphs

ℹ You need to know...

- **how to recognise and use the intercept and gradient of a graph of a linear equation.**

Linear equations take the form **y = m𝔁 + c** where m is equal to the **gradient** (slope) of the line, and c is equal to the **intercept** (the value of y at the point where the line crosses the y-axis). The values of m and c can be positive or negative, and it is important to include the + or − sign.

The gradient (m) can be calculated by creating a right-angled triangle on the graph line, and using the formula...

$$\text{gradient (m)} = \frac{\text{vertical distance}}{\text{horizontal distance}}$$

The larger the number the steeper the graph

To use the equation y = m𝔁 + c to draw a graph...

1. The equation may not be in the form y = m𝔁 + c, so you may need to rearrange it first.
2. From the equation, pick out the values of m and c.
3. Use the value of c to mark the intercept on the y axis – remember this may be a negative value.
4. From the intercept, go along 1 unit to the right and then up or down by the value of m (up for positive m and down for negative m). Mark a dot at this point.
5. From the intercept, repeat the last step, reversing the directions. Mark a dot at this point.
6. Draw a long line passing through all three points.

To find the equation of a straight line...

1. Find the intercept (c).
2. Find the gradient (m) by marking 2 accurate points on the line and using them to make a right-angled triangle:
   m = vertical distance ÷ horizontal distance.
3. If the line slopes from bottom left to top right, m is positive, if it slopes from top left to bottom right m is negative.
4. Insert the values for m and c into the equation y = m𝔁 + c.

Examples

1. Identify the intercept and the gradient of the graph y = 𝔁 + 2
   The intercept is at y = +2 and the gradient of the line is +1 (3 ÷ 3 = 1).

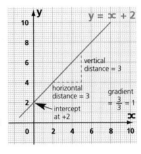

2. Draw the graph of 3𝔁 = y − 4

   First rearrange the equation...
   $$3𝔁 = y − 4$$
   $$3𝔁 + 4 = y − \cancel{4} + \cancel{4}$$
   $$y = 3𝔁 + 4$$

   Find m and c:
   $$y = m𝔁 + c$$
   $$y = 3𝔁 + 4$$
   m = +3 and c = +4

   Mark the points on the graph and draw the line.

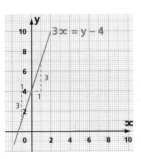

3. Find the equation of this straight line.
   The intercept is at y = +1 so c = +1.
   $$m = \frac{2}{4} = \frac{1}{2}$$
   The equation of the line is $y = \frac{1}{2}𝔁 + 1$

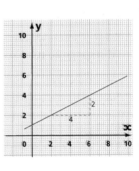

❓ Now try these...

1. Use y = m𝔁 + c to draw the graph of y = -2𝔁 − 2

2. Find the equation of this line.

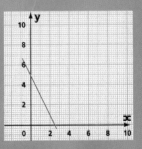

ℹ You need to know...

- **how to recognise and sketch graphs of linear, quadratic, cubic and reciprocal equations.**

Different types of equation produce different types of graph, and you must be able to identify the types of equations from the graphs.

Linear equations have no powers of x greater than 1, i.e. there may be an x term, but there will not be an x^2 term or any other power of x. Linear equations always produce a straight-line graph.

Quadratic equations have powers of x up to, but no greater than 2. A quadratic graph is a curve called a parabola. This is a symmetrical 'U'-shaped curve that may be the normal way around (∪) or upside down (∩).

Cubic equations have powers of x up to, but no greater than 3. Cubic curves have a shape like a large 'S'. They do not have a line of symmetry.

Reciprocal equations are in the form of a fraction, with x as the denominator, and where the numerator is a number other than 0. The graph of a reciprocal equation is symmetrical about the line $y = x$, and all reciprocal graphs have the same shape – they only vary in their distance from the origin.

Examples

Write down the type of graph you would expect each equation to produce and sketch the graph.

1 $y = 2x + 3$
Linear graph

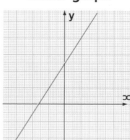

2 $y = x^2 + 2x - 1$
Quadratic graph

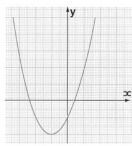

3 $y = x^3$
Cubic graph

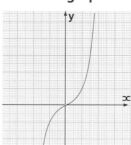

4 $y = \frac{2}{x}$
Reciprocal graph

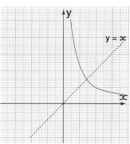

❓ Now try these...

Match each graph with its **possible** equation:

1 $y = x^3 + x^2 - x + 1$

2 $y = \frac{1}{2}x - 3$

3 $y = \frac{3}{x}$

4 $y = x^2 + 1$

a)

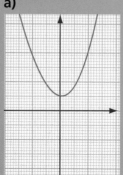

b)

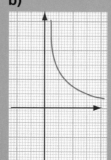

c)

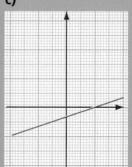

d)

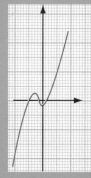

Example

a) Complete this table of values for
$y = x^2 + 2x - 1$.

x	-4	-3	-2	-1	0	1	2
y							

When $x = -4$, $y = 16 - 8 - 1 = 7$
When $x = -3$, $y = 9 - 6 - 1 = 2$
When $x = -2$, $y = 4 - 4 - 1 = -1$
When $x = -1$, $y = 1 - 2 - 1 = -2$
When $x = 0$, $y = 0 + 0 - 1 = -1$
When $x = 1$, $y = 1 + 2 - 1 = 2$
When $x = 2$, $y = 4 + 4 - 1 = 7$

x	-4	-3	-2	-1	0	1	2
y	7	2	-1	-2	-1	2	7

b) Use the values to draw the graph of
$y = x^2 + 2x - 1$.

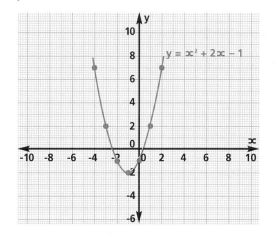

ℹ You need to know...

- **how to plot the graphs of quadratic equations.**

The method for drawing graphs of quadratic equations is basically the same as for linear equations. However, you will need more pairs of coordinates to draw the curve and finding the y values can be a bit trickier. You will probably be given values of x and asked to complete a table of values before you draw the graph.

The table of values is very important. If one value is wrong the whole graph will be wrong, so it is worth taking your time and making sure your working out is accurate.

When you have found all the y values, plot the points on your graph and join the points carefully to make a smooth curve – do not use a ruler for any part of the curve.

If the final graph does not look symmetrical you have made a mistake – check your working out and make sure you plotted the points correctly.

? Now try these...

1 a) Copy and complete this table of values for
$y = x^2 - 2x + 3$.

x	-1	0	1	2	3
y					

b) Use the table of values to draw the graph of
$y = x^2 - 2x + 3$.

2 a) Copy and complete this table of values for
$y = x^2 - 4$.

x	-3	-2	-1	0	1	2	3
y							

b) Use the table of values to draw the graph of
$y = x^2 - 4$.

i) You need to know...

- **how to solve simultaneous linear equations graphically.**

A pair of linear equations that have a common solution (i.e. values of x and y that work for both equations), are called **simultaneous equations**.

Some simultaneous equations can be solved using algebraic methods (see p.41). Others may be easier to solve by drawing a graph. The **solution** to the equations is found where the lines cross.

To solve simultaneous equations graphically...

1. Produce a table of values for each equation. The graphs will be straight lines so you will only need a few values – three should be enough.
2. Plot the points for the two lines on the same graph. You may need to extend one or both of the lines to give a crossing point.
3. Write down the coordinates of the point where the two lines cross.
4. The x and y coordinates of the crossing point are the solutions to the equations.

Example

Solve these simultaneous equations by drawing a graph: $y = 2x + 4$ and $y = 1 - x$

First produce tables of values:

$y = 2x + 4$

x	-2	0	2
y	0	4	8

$y = 1 - x$

x	-2	0	2
y	3	1	-1

Then draw the graph...

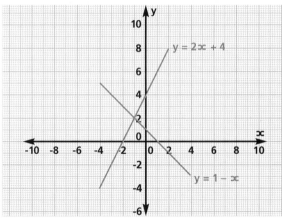

The coordinates of the crossing point are (-1,2), so the solution to the equations is $x = -1$ and y = 2.

? Now try these...

1. **a)** On a grid, draw the graphs of $y = x - 4$ and $y = 5 - 2x$.
   b) Use your graph to solve the simultaneous equations $y = x - 4$ and $y = 5 - 2x$.

2. **a)** On a grid, draw the graphs of $y = x$ and $y = \frac{1}{2}x + 1$.
   b) Use your graph to solve the simultaneous equations $y = x$ and $y = \frac{1}{2}x + 1$.

3. **a)** On a grid, draw the graphs of $y = x - 2$ and $y = -\frac{1}{2}x + 1$.
   b) Use your graph to solve the simultaneous equations $y = x - 2$ and $y = -\frac{1}{2}x + 1$.

4. **a)** On a grid, draw the graphs of $y = -\frac{1}{3}x - 6$ and $y = x + 2$.
   b) Use your graph to solve the simultaneous equations $y = -\frac{1}{3}x - 6$ and $y = x + 2$.

Graphs

You need to know...

- **how to interpret graphs that model real situations.**

Any situation where the value of one variable directly affects another variable can produce a graph. The graph may be accurately plotted, or it may be a sketch used to give a general idea of the relationship between the variables.

On sketch graphs...

- The axes are not numbered.
- A straight line rising from left to right represents variables that both increase proportionately.
- A slope falling from left to right shows that one variable decreases as the other increases.
- The gradient at a point on a curved line represents the rate at which one variable changes compared to the other.
- As well as looking at the shape of the graph, consider what the two axes represent.

In travel graphs...

- Time is plotted on the x axis and distance travelled is plotted on the y axis.
- The slope (gradient) of any section of the graph represents the average speed of the journey during that time. The greater the gradient, the faster the speed.
- Any horizontal (flat) sections of graph represent time when the traveller has stopped.

Examples

1. This sketch graph shows the height of a ball above the ground when it is thrown, plotted against the distance from the thrower.
   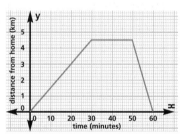
   a) What does the x-axis represent?
      It represents the distance from the thrower.
   b) Why does the graph start higher than 0 on the y-axis, but end up at 0?
      Because the ball was thrown from the thrower's hand, not from the ground, but it landed on the ground.

2. The graph shows John's journey to and from his grandma's house.
   a) How far away from John's home is his grandma's house?
      The greatest distance from home that John reaches is 4.5km.
   b) What was John's speed for the first part of his journey?

   The distance is 4.5km and it takes 30 minutes = $\frac{1}{2}$ hour

   speed = D ÷ T = 4.5 ÷ $\frac{1}{2}$ = 9km/h

Now try these...

1. Look at the sketch graphs. Which graph best matches each of these relationships?
   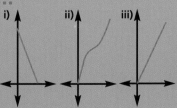
   a) The circumference of a circle and its diameter.
   b) The length of a rectangle with area 30cm² and its width.
   c) The distance a runner has run in a marathon and the time she has been running.

2. Use the graph in Example 2 for this question.
   a) How long did John stay at his grandma's house?
   b) How far did John travel altogether?
   c) Coming home the ride was all downhill. What was John's average speed on his home journey?

ⓘ You need to know...

- **how to solve simple inequalities using algebra.**

Inequalities are very similar to equations, but instead of an equals sign they have one of these four inequality signs…

> **>** greater than

> **<** less than

> **≥** greater than or equal to

> **≤** less than or equal to

Inequalities can be shown on a number line to illustrate the range of values that are included. The expression with the smaller value is always written at the small (pointed) end of the sign. When solving an inequality you are not finding a single value for the variable, you are finding a range of possible values to fit the rule.

To solve an inequality using algebra, treat it like an equation – all the normal rules of algebra still apply, so whatever you do to one side you must also do to the other. There is one exception to this – when you multiply or divide by a negative number, the inequality sign must be reversed.

Examples

① Show the inequality $-3 < x \leqslant 2$ on a number line:

> Use a closed circle for ⩽ and ⩾ and an open circle for < and >.

② Write down all the integer values of x that satisfy the inequality $-3 \leqslant x < 5$.

The inequality means that 'x can take any value between -3 and 5, including -3 but not 5'. An integer is a whole number, so the possible values for x **are -3, -2, -1, 0, 1, 2, 3, and 4.**

③ Solve the inequality $3x + 2 > 8$

$$3x + 2 > 8$$
$$3x + 2 - 2 > 8 - 2$$
$$3x > 6$$
$$\frac{3x}{3} > \frac{6}{3}$$
$$x > 2$$

④ Solve the inequality $5 - 2x < 1$

$$5 - 2x < 1$$
$$5 - 2x - 5 < 1 - 5$$
$$-2x < -4$$
$$\frac{-2x}{-2} > \frac{-4}{-2}$$
$$x > 2$$

> Divide by -2 so reverse the inequality

❓ Now try these...

1 Draw a number line to show the inequality $-5 \leqslant x < 4$

2 Write down all the integer values of x that satisfy the inequality $-9 < x < 0$

3 Solve these inequalities using algebra:

a) $x + 5 \geqslant 11$ d) $8 - 4x < 12$

b) $7x - 2 \leqslant 8$ e) $7 > 4x + 15$

c) $3x + 12 > 0$ f) $3 + x > 2x$

Solving Inequalities

ℹ You need to know...

- **how to solve simple inequalities by drawing graphs.**

The solution to an inequality is always a range of possible values. In algebra this is shown by using an inequality sign, but on a graph it is represented by shading the region (area) of the graph where the possible solutions lie.

To draw graphs of inequalities...

1. write down each inequality
2. write them down again, changing the inequality signs to equals signs
3. make a table of values for each equation (remember you only need 3 values for a straight line graph)
4. draw the lines for each equation, all on the same graph
5. if the original equality used the signs > or <, the line on the graph should be dotted, if it used ⩾ or ⩽, draw a solid line (the dotted line indicates that the values along the line are **not** included in the area).
6. shade the area that is enclosed by the lines.

Examples

1. Draw a graph and shade the region that satisfies the inequalities $y < 4$, $y ⩾ x + 2$ and $x ⩾ -2$.

   Write as equations...
   $y < 4$ becomes $y = 4$
   $y ⩾ x + 2$ becomes $y = x + 2$
   $x ⩾ -2$ becomes $x = -2$
   Table of values for $y = x + 2$:

x	-1	0	1
y	1	2	3

   Draw and shade the graph...

   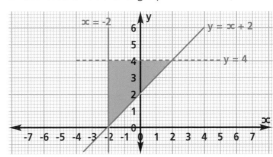

   All the possible solutions to the inequality lie within the shaded region.

2. Draw a graph and shade the region that satisfies the inequalities $x + y ⩽ 4$, $x ⩾ 1$ and $y ⩾ 0$.

   Write them all as equations...
   $x + y = 4$, $x = 1$ and $y = 0$
   Table of values for $x + y = 4$...

   rearrange the equation first: $y = 4 - x$

x	-1	0	1
y	5	4	3

   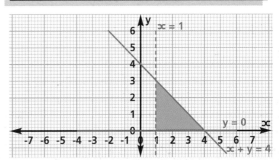

❓ Now try these...

1. Draw a graph and shade the region that satisfies these inequalities... $y < x$, $y ⩾ -2$ and $x + y < 2$.

2. Draw a graph and shade the region that satisfies these inequalities... $y < 3 - x$, $y > x$ and $x ⩾ -2$.

3. Draw a graph and shade the region that satisfies these inequalities... $x + y < 12$, $y < 6$, $x ⩾ 0$ and $y ⩾ 0$.

✓ You should already know...

- **the metric and imperial measurements of length, mass and capacity**
- **how to convert measurements within the same system.**

ⓘ You also need to know...

- **the rough metric equivalents of imperial units still in daily use.**

The tables below give acceptable equivalent values for metric and imperial measurements.
The symbol ≈ means 'approximately equal to'.

Length

1 inch ≈ 2.5cm
1 foot ≈ 30cm
1 yard ≈ 91cm
1 mile ≈ 1.6km
(Remember a 30cm ruler is about a foot long)

Mass

1 ounce ≈ 28g
1 pound ≈ 454g
1 stone ≈ 6.4kg
1 ton is a bit more than 1 tonne
(Remember that a bag of sugar weighs 1kg, which is about 2.2lbs)

Capacity

1 pint ≈ 0.6 litres
1 gallon ≈ 4.5 litres
(Remember: a litre of water is a pint and three quarters.)

Examples

① Convert 35 miles into km.
$$\textbf{1 mile} \approx \textbf{1.6km}$$
so   **35 miles ≈ 35 x 1.6 = 56km**

② Convert 750g to pounds.
$$\textbf{454g} \approx \textbf{1lb}$$
so   **750g ≈ 750 x 454 = 1.6lbs**

③ Convert 14 gallons to l.
$$\textbf{1 gallon} \approx \textbf{4.5l}$$
so **14 gallons ≈ 14 x 4.5 = 63l**

❓ Now try these...

1. Convert 75cm into inches.
2. Roughly how many ounces are there in 200g?
3. Convert 15l into gallons.
4. Roughly how many cm are there in $4\frac{1}{2}$ feet?
5. Convert 64kg into pounds.
6. Roughly how many pints are there in 3.6l?
7. Which is heavier: a tonne of feathers or a tonne of bricks?
8. Which is the longest distance to run: a marathon (26.2 miles) or 40km?

Example

One pound is equal to 0.45kg.

a) Draw a conversion graph for pounds and kilograms.

Start by producing a table of values:

lbs	0	1	2	3	4	5	6
	0.45x0	0.45x1	0.45x2	0.45x3	0.45x4	0.45x5	0.45x6
kg	0	0.45	0.9	1.35	1.8	2.25	2.7

Use the table of values to plot a graph.

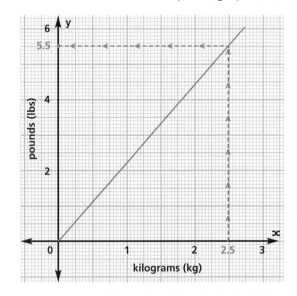

b) Approximately how many pounds is 2.5kg?

We can use the conversion graph to find out the value in pounds. Simply draw a line up from the 2.5kg mark on the x-axis to the line, then across to the y-axis, we can see that it is roughly equal to **5.5lbs**.

ⓘ You need to know...

- **how to use graphs to convert one unit of measurement to another.**

If the equivalent values of two units (such as inches and centimetres, or two different currencies) are known, a graph can be constructed to show this information. The graph can then be used to convert other values. This type of graph is called a **conversion graph**.

? Now try these...

① £1 is worth about €1.45 (although this changes every day!).

a) Complete this conversion table.

b) Draw a conversion graph with £ horizontally from £0 to £5 and € vertically from €0 to €8.

£	0	1	2	3	4	5
€	0	1.45		4.35		

c) Use your graph to convert £3.50 to €.

d) Use your graph to convert €6 to £.

e) Can you use your graph to convert £50 to €?

You need to know...

- **how to read and interpret scales on a range of measuring equipment with appropriate accuracy.**

The divisions on these scales represent smaller numbers, so you can make more accurate readings.

each division is 0.01 unit

When the indicator lies between two divisions, you can estimate a reading or round up depending on the level of accuracy you are asked for.

You could estimate the reading on these weighing scales as 1385g or give it as 1390g to the nearest 10g.

Examples

1 What value is shown by each of the arrows?

Arrow A shows 3.53
Arrow B shows 3.62
Arrow C shows 3.44

2 What value is shown by each of the arrows?

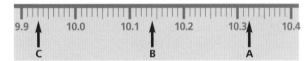

Arrow A shows 10.32
Arrow B shows 10.14
Arrow C shows 9.93

3 Estimate the values shown by the arrows on the scale.

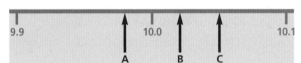

Arrow A shows about 9.98
Arrow B shows about 10.02
Arrow C shows about 10.05

? Now try these...

1 Estimate the values shown by the arrows on the scales below.

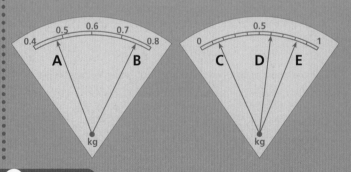

2 Put these arrows on the scale:

Arrow A at 7.9   Arrow B at 8.85
Arrow C at 5.65   Arrow D at 7.05

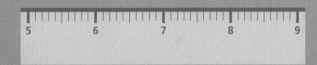

3 Give the values shown by the arrows on the scale.

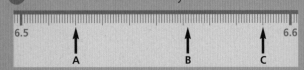

Measurement

Example

The tree is 10m tall. Estimate the heights of the other objects.

If you get a question like this in an exam, there won't be a scale alongside the drawing. However, you can sketch your own if it helps.

The pylon is about 25m tall.
The block of flats is about 20m tall.
The bird is flying at about 30m.
The helicopter is flying at about 35m.

ℹ You need to know...

- **how to make sensible estimates of a range of measures in relation to everyday situations.**

If you are asked to estimate a quantity or measurement, you need to apply some common sense.

Try to make comparisons with objects that you know the size of, e.g. a standard ruler measures approximately 30cm and a bag of sugar weighs 1 kilogram.

Make sure you always use a sensible unit of measurement for your estimates.

For example, look at this book. You can see that the length of the book is roughly the same as the length of a ruler. Therefore, 30cm would be a good estimate.

❓ Now try these...

1. Make sensible estimates for the following measures:
   a) the mass of a house brick.
   b) the height of your bedroom door.
   c) the amount of water in a window cleaner's bucket when it is full.
   d) the height of your school desk.
   e) the height of the worksurface in your kitchen at home.
   f) the diameter of a CD.

2. This line is 5cm long.

   Estimate the lengths of these lines.

   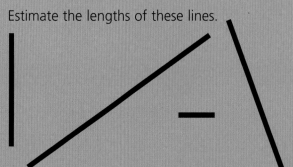

i You need to know...

- **that measurements given to the nearest whole number may be inaccurate by up to one half in either direction.**

Think about how decimals get rounded to a whole number (see p. 36). If the digit after the decimal point is 5 or more, the number is rounded up. If the digit is less than 5, the number stays the same.

Measurements are often given to the nearest unit in the same way. For example, on the case of a DVD it might say the running time is 180 minutes. However, the manufacturers will have given the time to the nearest minute, so it could be inaccurate by up to half a minute either way. That is to say, if you recorded the exact running time of the DVD with a stop watch, it could be 179.5 minutes or above but less than 180.5 minutes.

This range is called an interval and can be written using inequalities.

Examples

1 A leaf is measured as 46cm long to the nearest cm.

a) What are the smallest and largest values that can be rounded to 46cm?

Smallest = 45.5cm
Largest = just less than 46.5cm

> because 46.5cm would be rounded to 47cm

b) Using inequalities write the interval in which the true length of the leaf must lie.

45.5 ⩽ L < 46.5

> meaning length (L) is equal to or greater than 45.5cm and less than 46.5cm

2 Another leaf is measured to be 46.2cm long to the nearest 0.1cm.

a) What are the smallest and largest values that could be rounded to 46.2cm?

Smallest = 46.15cm
Largest = just less than 46.25cm.

b) Using inequalities write the interval in which the true length of the leaf must lie.

46.15 ⩽ L < 46.25

? Now try these...

1 A concrete block is weighed as 26kg correct to the nearest kg.
  a) What are the minimum and maximum values of the weight of the block?
  b) Using inequalities write the interval in which the true weight must lie.
2 A rod is measured to be 13.7cm correct to the nearest 0.1cm.
  a) What are the lower and upper values of the length of the rod?

  b) Using inequalities write the interval in which the true length of the rod must lie.
3 A football match is attended by 32 400 people correct to the nearest 100 people.
  a) What are the minimum and maximum values for the actual number of people attending?
  b) Using inequalities write the interval in which the true attendance figure must lie.

Measurement

You need to know...

- **how to use compound measures such as density.**

Compound measures combine two different measurements.

Density is a compound measure. It is a measure of how heavy an object is (mass) in relation to its size (volume). Density is measured in kilograms per cubic metre (kg/m^3) or grams per cubic centimetre (g/cm^3). The formula for density is...

$$\text{Density (D)} = \frac{\text{Mass (M)}}{\text{Volume (V)}}$$

and can be put in a formula triangle...

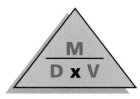

To use the formula triangle put your finger over the part you want to find. The letters left uncovered will tell you how to find it.

The units of measurement for a compound measure tell you how it is calculated. For example, density is measured in grams per cubic centimetre...

$$g/cm^3 = \frac{\text{grams}}{cm^3} \text{ or } \frac{\text{Mass}}{\text{Volume}}$$

Examples

1 An object weighs 15kg and has a volume of $2.5m^3$. What is its density?

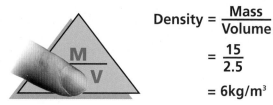

$$\text{Density} = \frac{\text{Mass}}{\text{Volume}}$$
$$= \frac{15}{2.5}$$
$$= 6kg/m^3$$

2 What is the volume of a 210g block of density $15g/cm^3$?

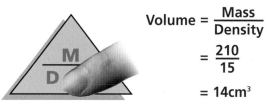

$$\text{Volume} = \frac{\text{Mass}}{\text{Density}}$$
$$= \frac{210}{15}$$
$$= 14cm^3$$

3 What is the mass of a substance of density $25.6g/cm^3$ and volume $300cm^3$?

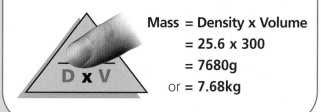

$$\text{Mass} = \text{Density x Volume}$$
$$= 25.6 \times 300$$
$$= 7680g$$
$$\text{or} = 7.68kg$$

Now try these...

1 Copy and complete this table.

Density	Mass	Volume
	10kg	$1.25m^3$
$1.5g/cm^3$	750g	
$9g/cm^3$		$16cm^3$
	69kg	$7m^3$
$12g/cm^3$		$30cm^3$

i You need to know...

* **how to use compound measures such as speed.**

Speed is another compound measure. It combines measures of distance and time.

Speed can be measured in kilometres per hour (km/h) or metres per second (m/s) but miles per hour (mph) is the most common unit in daily life. Make sure you have the correct units before performing your calculation! The formula for speed is

$$\text{Speed (S)} = \frac{\text{Distance (D)}}{\text{Time (T)}}$$

and can be put in a formula triangle…

Examples

1. A car travels 60km in 2 hours. What is its speed?

$$\text{Speed} = \frac{\text{Distance}}{\text{Time}}$$
$$= \frac{60}{2}$$
$$= 30\text{km/h}$$

2. A bird flies at 10m/s. How far will it fly in half an hour?

Half an hour = 30 minutes
30 minutes x 60 = 1800 seconds

Distance = Speed x Time
= 10 x 1800
= 18 000m
or = 18km

3. A girl walks at 3km/h. How long will it take her to walk 26km?

$$\text{Time} = \frac{\text{Distance}}{\text{Speed}}$$
$$= \frac{26}{3}$$
$$= 8.6666 \text{ hours}$$

0.666 hours needs to be converted into minutes…
0.666 x 60 = 40 minutes

Time = 8 hours 40 minutes

? Now try these...

1. Copy and complete this table.

Speed	Distance	Time
	15km	3 hours
25m/s		15 seconds
650km/h	2210km	

Remember to convert any decimal parts in answers into minutes by multiplying by 60.

2. A car travels 184 miles in 4 hours. What is its speed?

3. A woman runs a marathon (26 miles) in 4 hours and 40 minutes. What is her speed?

4. If I walk at 4 miles an hour, how long will it take me to walk 6 miles?

ℹ️ You need to know...

- **how to interpret travel graphs.**

A travel graph is a visual representation of a journey. All travel graphs have time on the x-axis. The y-axis shows the distance of the object from the origin (starting point).

This means that a journey which starts and finishes at the same place, e.g. a runner completing one circuit of a running track, will produce a graph that starts and finishes at 0 on the y-axis.

Travel graphs can be used to calculate the speed of an object at a given point, by finding the gradient of the graph at that point.

Example

Look at the graph below. It shows a cyclist travelling to the shops and then back home again.

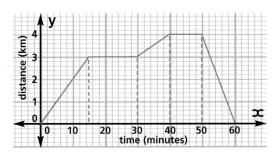

a) At what speed was the cyclist travelling in the first 15 minutes?

> The cyclist travelled 3km in 15 minutes ($\frac{1}{4}$ hour or 0.25)

$$\text{Speed} = \frac{\text{Distance}}{\text{Time}} = \frac{3}{0.25} = 12\text{km/h}$$

b) At what speed was the cyclist travelling between 30 and 40 minutes?

> The cyclist travelled 1km in 10 minutes ($\frac{1}{6}$ hour or 0.167)

$$\text{Speed} = \frac{\text{Distance}}{\text{Time}} = \frac{1}{0.167} = 6\text{km/h}$$

c) Which parts of the graph indicate that the cyclist stopped moving? And how long did he stop for each time?

> The **horizontal (flat)** parts of the graph indicate when the cyclist was stationary, first for **15 minutes** then for **10 minutes**.

d) The graph is steepest between 50 and 60 minutes. What does this tell you about the cyclist's speed at this point?

> **The steepest part of the graph is where the cyclist was travelling fastest.**

e) At what speed was the cyclist travelling in the last 10 minutes of his journey?

> The cyclist travelled 1km in 10 minutes ($\frac{1}{6}$ hour or 0.167)

$$\text{Speed} = \frac{\text{Distance}}{\text{Time}} = \frac{4}{0.167} = 24\text{km/h}$$

❓ Now try these...

1 The graph opposite shows a vehicle's journey.
  a) For how long is the vehicle stationary?
  b) What is the speed of the vehicle on the final part of its journey in metres per second?
  c) Copy and complete the travel graph, if the vehicle remains stationary for 20 seconds and then returns to its starting point in 1 minute exactly.

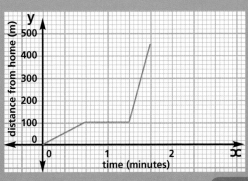

You should already know...

- that there are 360° in a full turn, 180° in a half turn and 90° in a quarter turn
- that acute angles are less than 90°, obtuse angles are between 90° and 180° and reflex angles are over 180°
- that an angle of 90° is called a right angle.

 You also need to know...

- the properties of angles on a straight line and at a point
- that the angles in a triangle add up to 180°.

Angles on a straight line add up to 180°.
a + b = 180°

Angles at a point add up to 360°.
a + b + c + d = 360°

When two straight lines intersect (i.e. cross), the angles opposite each other are equal. **a = c** and **b = d**. These are called **vertically opposite angles**.

Notice also that:
a + b = 180°
b + c = 180°
c + d = 180°
a + d = 180°
} These are all angles on a straight line

and
a + b + c + d = 360° = the angles around a point.

Angles in a triangle add up to 180°.
a + b + c = 180°

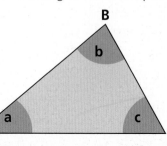

Examples

Work out the value of x in each of the following:

1 $x + 30° = 180°$
$x = 180° - 30°$
$x = 150°$

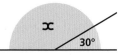

2 $x + 65° + 90° = 180°$
$x + 155° = 180°$
$x = 180° - 155°$
$x = 25°$

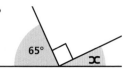

3 $x + 62° + 80° = 360°$
$x + 142° = 360°$
$x = 360° - 142°$
$x = 218°$

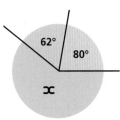

4 Work out the values of x, y and z.

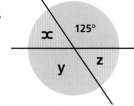

$x + 125° = 180°$
$x = 180° - 125°$ on a straight line
$x = 55°$
$y = 125°$ vertically opposite
$z = x$ vertically opposite
$z = 55°$

check: **55° + 55° + 125° + 125° = 360°**

5 $x + 55° + 60° = 180°$
$x + 115° = 180°$
$x = 180° - 115°$
$x = 65°$

Angles

You need to know...

- **the properties of corresponding, alternate and co-interior angles.**

When a straight line crosses two or more **parallel lines** it is called a **traversal** and new angles are created.

Alternate Angles

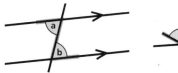 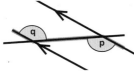

Alternate angles are always equal in size. Alternate angles can be easily spotted because they form a letter **Z** (although sometimes it may be reversed, **Ƨ**!!).

Corresponding Angles

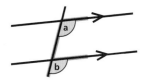 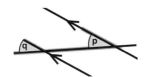

Corresponding angles are always equal in size. Corresponding angles can be easily spotted because they form a letter **F** (although sometimes it may be reversed, **Ⅎ**, or upside down **Ⴓ, Ⴇ**!!)

Co-Interior Angles

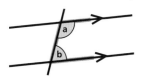 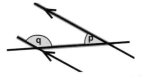

Co-interior angles always add up to 180°. Co-interior angles can be easily spotted because they form a letter **⊏** or **⊔** (although sometimes it may be reversed, **⊐** or **⊓**!!).
Co-interior angles are sometimes called 'supplementary' or 'allied' angles.

Example

Work out the value of each of the letters in the diagram.

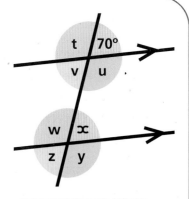

$t + 70° = 180°$ angles on a straight line
$t = 180° - 70°$
$t = 110°$

$u = t = 110°$ vertically opposite angles
$v = 70°$ vertically opposite angles
$w = u = 110°$ alternate angles

$x + u = 180°$ co-interior angles
$x + 110° = 180°$
$x = 180° - 110°$
$x = 70°$

$y = w = 110°$ vertically opposite angles
$z = v = 70°$ corresponding angles

? Now try these...

Find the angles marked with letters.

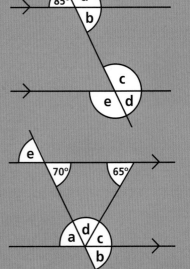

You need to know...

- the properties of angles in quadrilaterals
- the properties of angles in polygons.

Quadrilaterals

A quadrilateral is a shape with 4 sides. The **interior** angles in all **quadrilaterals** add up to 360°.

a + b + c + d = 360°

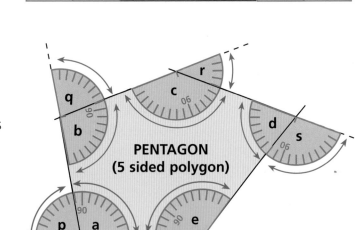

QUADRILATERAL

Polygons

A polygon is any shape with 3 or more sides. The **exterior** angles of any **polygon** add up to 360° (a full turn). In regular polygons, all exterior angles are equal. In regular polygons...

each exterior angle = $\dfrac{360}{n}$
(where n is the number of sides)

Notice also that for all polygons...

each interior angle + exterior angle = 180°
(angles on a straight line again!)

PENTAGON
(5 sided polygon)

Example

Calculate angles x and y in this regular octagon.

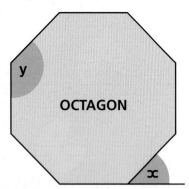

OCTAGON

An octagon has 8 sides, so...

$x = \dfrac{360°}{8} = 45°$ 　　　$x + y = 180°$

　　　　　　　　　　　$45° + y = 180°$

　　　　　　　　　　　$y = 180° - 45°$

　　　　　　　　　　　$y = 135°$

? Now try these...

1 Calculate angle x in this quadrilateral.

x

85°

52°

2 Calculate angles x and y in this regular hexagon.

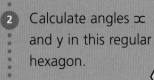

y

x

ℹ You need to know...

- **how to measure and draw angles.**

A protractor is used to measure angles. Most protractors are semi-circular and measure from 0° to 180°, but some are full circles and can go up to 360°. Many have two scales on them so they can be used to measure from the left or the right – this is where confusion can arise.

Example

How many degrees is this angle?

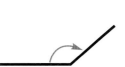
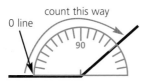

It is clearly an obtuse angle, i.e. it is between 90° and 180°. Place the protractor over the angle, making sure the cross is over the corner of the angle and zero is lined up with the baseline of the angle. Count up the scale until you get to the other line. **The angle measures 140°.**

To draw angles...

1 Draw a baseline about 5-6cm long. Mark a cross at one end.

2 Place your protractor on the line so the cross of the protractor is exactly above the cross on the end of the line.

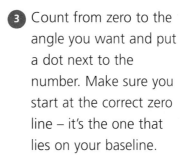

3 Count from zero to the angle you want and put a dot next to the number. Make sure you start at the correct zero line – it's the one that lies on your baseline.

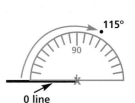

4 Remove the protractor and carefully join the dot to the centre of the cross. Finally, check the angle with your protractor.

❓ Now try these...

1 Measure these angles.

a)
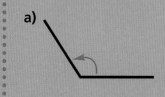

b)
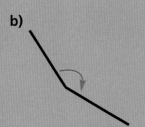

c)

d)

Hint: Measure the acute angle then subtract it from 360° to get the **reflex** angle.

2 Measure the angles in this triangle. Check that they add up to 180° - you may be 1° or 2° out!

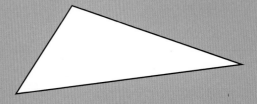

3 Draw the following angles...
   a) 35°   **b)** 110°   **c)** 147°   **d)** 300°

Hint: what is 360° – 300°? Can you draw this angle more easily? Which part will you label '300°'?

Thurstonland

Example

Write down the coordinates of the points marked with letters.

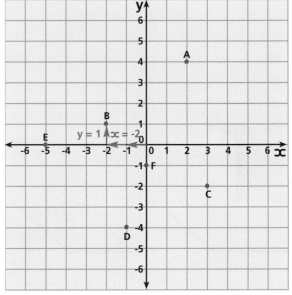

A = (2,4)   D = (-1,-4)

B = (-2,1)   E = (-5,0)

C = (3,-2)   F = (0,-1)

✓ **You should already know...**

- that one coordinate identifies a point on a number line
- that two coordinates (x,y) identify a point on a plane.

ⓘ **You also need to know...**

- how to use axes and coordinates to identify points in all four quadrants.

When the x and y axes include negative values, the coordinates are still written as (x,**y**), but care must be taken not to miss out or ignore any minus (-) signs. The axes divide the grid into four 'sections'. These sections are called **quadrants**.

? **Now try these...**

1 Draw axes with x values from -8 to 8 and y values from -8 to 8. On your grid plot and label these points:

A (-5,2)
B (4,3)
C (0,-6)
D (-3,-3)
E (7,3)
F (-4,-1)
G (-3,0)
H (-6,8)

2 Write down the coordinates of the points marked with letters on the grid alongside.

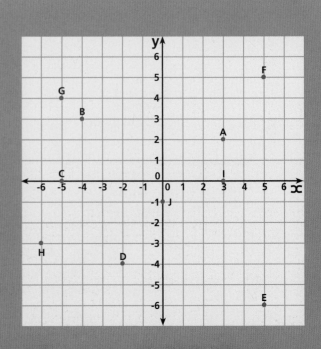

Coordinates

ℹ You need to know...

- **that three coordinates identify a point in 3-D.**

Two coordinates (x,y) allow you to describe the location of a point in a plane, i.e. in 2-D, because they provide you with two directions (left-right, up-down).

By adding a third coordinate (z) you introduce a third direction (forwards-backwards), which allows you to describe the location of a point in three-dimensional space, i.e. 3-D. The coordinates of a point in 3-D are given by (x,y,z)

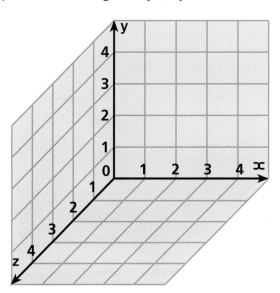

? Now try these...

1   Write down the coordinates of each vertex.

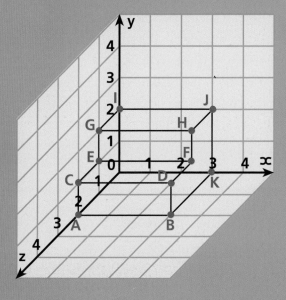

Example

A cuboid is plotted on the axes below. Write down the coordinates of each vertex.

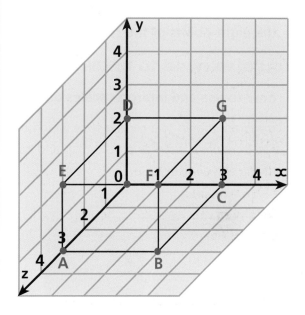

0 - is at the origin. **(0,0,0)**
A - is 3 units along the z-axis. **(0,0,3)**
B - is 3 units along the x-axis and 3 along the z-axis. **(3,0,3)**
C - is 3 units along the x-axis. **(3,0,0)**
D - is 2 units along the y-axis. **(0,2,0)**
E - is 2 units along the y-axis and 3 along the z-axis. **(0,2,3)**
F - is 3 units along the x-axis, 2 along the y-axis and 3 along the z-axis. **(3,2,3)**
G - is 3 units along the x-axis and 2 along the y-axis. **(3,2,0)**

2   **a)** Draw a cube with side lengths of 2 units using 3-D axes like the ones in the example.
  b) Label each of the corners and write down the coordinates in the form (x,y,z).

✓ You should already know...

- **that direction can be specified using clockwise/anti-clockwise turns and degrees**
- **that direction can also be specified using the eight points of the compass.**

ⓘ You also need to know...

- **how to use and interpret scales on maps.**

All maps are drawn to a certain scale which enables you to measure a distance on the map and calculate what the actual distance is.

Some examples of map scales are...

- **1cm = 1km** - every 1cm you measure on the map represents 1km on the ground.
- **1:50 000** - every 1cm you measure on the map represents 50 000cm (or 500m) on the ground. Or, if you measure in inches, every inch you measure on the map represents 50 000 inches (about 1380 yards) on the ground.

Examples

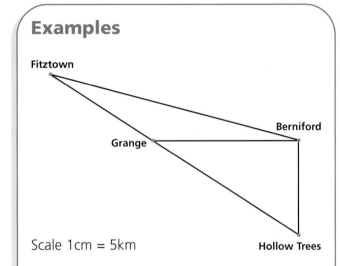

Scale 1cm = 5km

1 How far is it from Fitztown to Berniford?

On the map it is **7cm**, so **7 x 5 = 35km**.

2 I travel from Grange to Hollow Trees via Berniford. How much longer is this route than travelling directly from Grange to Hollow Trees?

Grange to Berniford is **4cm** Berniford to Hollow Trees is **2.5cm**	4 + 2.5 = 6.5cm 6.5 x 5 = 32.5km
Directly from Grange to Hollow Trees is **4.8cm**	4.8cm x 5 = 24km

So it is **32.5 – 24 = 8.5km longer**.

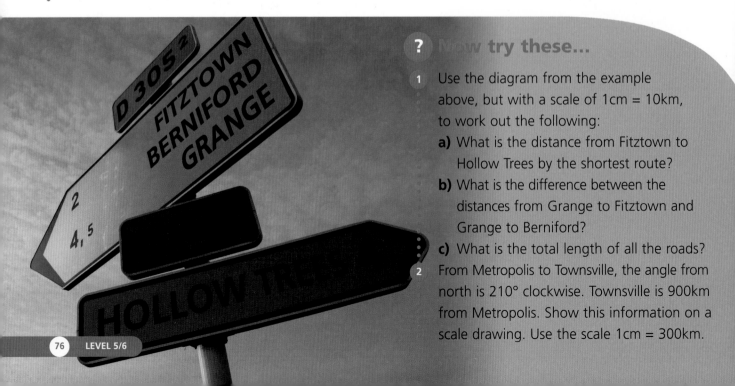

❓ Now try these...

1 Use the diagram from the example above, but with a scale of 1cm = 10km, to work out the following:

a) What is the distance from Fitztown to Hollow Trees by the shortest route?

b) What is the difference between the distances from Grange to Fitztown and Grange to Berniford?

c) What is the total length of all the roads?

2 From Metropolis to Townsville, the angle from north is 210° clockwise. Townsville is 900km from Metropolis. Show this information on a scale drawing. Use the scale 1cm = 300km.

Location

ⓘ You need to know...

- **how to use bearings to specify direction.**

When travelling, we rely on signposts and landmarks to find our way. However, in the air or at sea there is little to inform you of your location so navigators use bearings to find their way.

Bearings are a type of angle. However, they are always measured from north in a clockwise direction and are always given as 3 digits.

Remember the rules for angles on parallel lines? They can also be used when calculating bearings.

Examples

① What bearing is Andrew travelling on?

Andrew is travelling on a bearing of 059°.

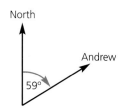

② Give the bearing of B from A, and A from B.

> 180° − 115° = 65°
> (co-interior angles)
> 360° − 65° = 295°

The bearing of B from A is 115°. The bearing of A from B is 295°.

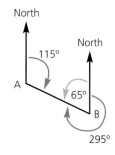

③ What bearing is Charlie travelling on?

> Small angles are easier to measure so the bearing can be calculated as
> **360° − 70° = 290°**

Charlie is travelling on a bearing of 290°.

④ Give the bearing of D from C, and C from D.

The bearing of D from C is 105°. The bearing of C from D is 285°.

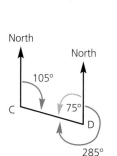

? Now try these...

For the following diagrams, give the bearing of:
a) Y from X
b) X from Y

①
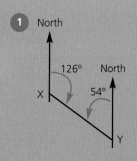

②
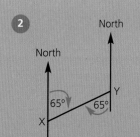

③
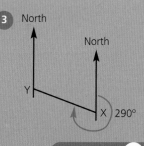

✓ You should already know...

- **the properties of quadrilaterals, including squares, rectangles, rhombi, parallelograms, trapeziums and kites.**

ⓘ You also need to know...

- **the properties of different triangles.**

A triangle is a shape that has three sides.

Scalene Triangles	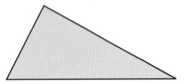	• No equal sides and no equal angles. • No lines of symmetry. • No rotational symmetry.
Isosceles Triangles	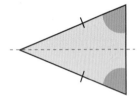	• Two equal sides and two equal angles. • One line of symmetry. • No rotational symmetry.
Equilateral Triangles	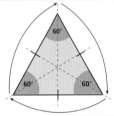	• Three equal sides and three equal angles (60°). • Three lines of symmetry. • Rotational symmetry of order 3.
Right-angled Triangles		• No equal sides and no equal angles. • No lines of symmetry. • No rotational symmetry ... unless it is also an isosceles triangle. 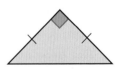

? Now try these...

1 Draw the following triangles and where applicable, indicate the lines of symmetry.
   a) An equilateral triangle of side 4cm.
   b) A right-angled isosceles triangle with the equal sides of length 5cm.

2 What type of triangle are the following statements describing?
   a) I have two equal sides, two equal angles and one line of symmetry.
   b) I have no equal angles, no equal sides, no lines of symmetry and none of my angles are 90°.
   c) I have three equal sides and three equal angles.

2-D Shapes

ⓘ You need to know...

- **about the properties of regular polygons.**

A **polygon** is a 2-D shape with many sides. Regular polygons have all their sides equal and all their angles equal. Here are the names and properties of the first few regular polygons. A regular triangle is an **equilateral triangle** (see facing page.) A regular quadrilateral is a **square**.

Regular Pentagon			• Five equal sides and five equal angles. • Five lines of symmetry. • Rotational symmetry of order 5.
Regular Hexagon		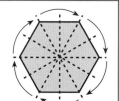	• Six equal sides and six equal angles. • Six lines of symmetry. • Rotational symmetry of order 6.
Regular Heptagon		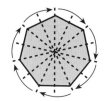	• Seven equal sides and seven equal angles. • Seven lines of symmetry. • Rotational symmetry of order 7.
Regular Octagon	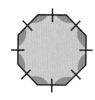	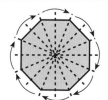	• Eight equal sides and eight equal angles. • Eight lines of symmetry. • Rotational symmetry of order 8.
Regular Nonagon		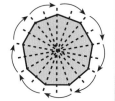	• Nine equal sides and nine equal angles. • Nine lines of symmetry. • Rotational symmetry of order 9.
Regular Decagon		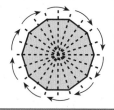	• Ten equal sides and ten equal angles. • Ten lines of symmetry. • Rotational symmetry of order 10.

Examples

1 What is the area of this rectangle?

Area = ℓ x w
Area = 7 x 4
Area = 28cm²

4cm

7cm

2 What is the area of this triangle?

The area of a triangle is half the area of a rectangle

6cm

5cm

Area of rectangle = ℓ x w
so **Area of triangle = $\frac{\ell \, x \, w}{2}$**

Area = $\frac{6 \, x \, 5}{2}$

Area = $\frac{30}{2}$

Area = 15cm²

✓ **You should already know...**

- that the perimeter of a shape can be found by adding together the lengths of all its edges
- that the area of a shape can be found by counting the total number of squares it covers on a grid
- that area is measured in square units, e.g. cm².

ⓘ **You also need to know...**

- the formula for finding the area of a rectangle and how to use it.

The standard formula for finding the area of a rectangle is:

Area = length x width
or **A = ℓ x w**

Area

w

ℓ

To calculate the area of this rectangle:

Area = ℓ x w
Area = 5cm x 3cm
Area = 15cm²

3cm

5cm

To prove the formula works, count the number of 1cm² squares that fit into the rectangle. You will see there are **3 rows of 5 squares**, which is **15** in total. Remember, in maths 'of' means 'multiply'. This is where the formula comes from.

? **Now try these...**

Find the area of each shape.

1

23cm

2cm

2

5m

20m

3

4cm

8cm

Area

i You need to know...

- **how to calculate the area of 2-D shapes.**

The area of a **parallelogram** can be found using the formula...

A = b x h

The area of a **trapezium** can be found using the formula...

A = ½ x (a+b) x h

The area of a **kite** can be found using the formula...

A = ½ x d x D

Compare this to the formula for finding the area of a triangle

Examples

Calculate the areas of these shapes...

①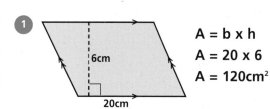
A = b x h
A = 20 x 6
A = 120cm²

②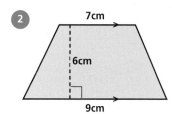
A = ½ x (a+b) x h
A = ½ x (7+9) x 6
A = ½ x 16 x 6
A = 48cm²

④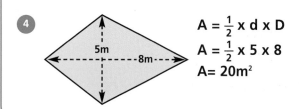
A = ½ x d x D
A = ½ x 5 x 8
A= 20m²

? Now try these...

① Find the area of these 2-D shapes.

a)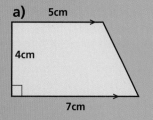
b)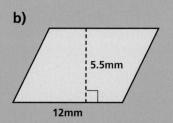
c)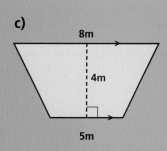
d)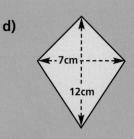

② Find the area of this rhombus.

Hint: you will have to break it down into four right-angled triangles as shown.

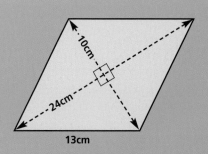

③ A parallelogram has an area of 60cm². Its vertical height is 8cm. What is the length of the base?

ℹ You need to know...

- **how to use the formulae for finding the area and circumference of a circle.**

It's important to know the names of the different parts of a circle.

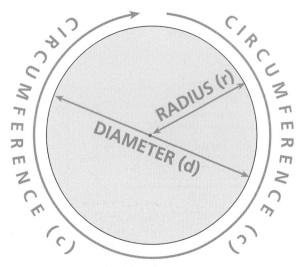

The circumference can be found using the formula:

> **Circumference = 2πr or πd**

The area of a circle is given by the formula:

> **Area = πr²**

π (pi) is simply a number: 3.141592653.... If you are not told the value for π in the question use the π button on your calculator, or 3.14.

Examples

Find the area and circumference of these circles.

1

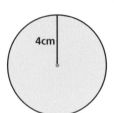

4cm

$$\text{Area} = \pi \times r^2$$
$$= \pi \times 4^2$$
$$= 3.14 \times 16$$
$$= 50.24\text{cm}^2$$

$$\text{Circumference} = 2 \times \pi \times r$$
$$= 2 \times \pi \times 4$$
$$= 2 \times 3.14 \times 4$$
$$= 25.12\text{cm}$$

2

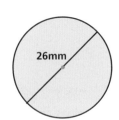

26mm

$r = \dfrac{d}{2}$

$$\text{Area} = \pi \times r^2$$
$$= \pi \times 13^2$$
$$= 3.14 \times 169$$
$$= 530.66\text{mm}^2$$

$$\text{Circumference} = \pi \times d$$
$$= \pi \times 26$$
$$= 81.64\text{mm}$$

❓ Now try these...

1 Find the area and circumference of these circles. Watch the units!

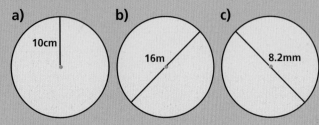

a) 10cm   b) 16m   c) 8.2mm

2 Find the area and total perimeter of this semicircle.

> **Hint:** Find the area and circumference of the full circle then divide by two. Don't forget to add on the straight edge to get the perimeter.

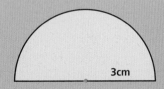

3cm

Area

ⓘ You need to know...

- **how to calculate the areas of compound shapes.**

Some 2-D shapes are made up of several standard shapes joined together. These are called **compound shapes**.

To calculate the area of a compound shape, break it down into shapes you know, work out the areas of the shapes and add them together.

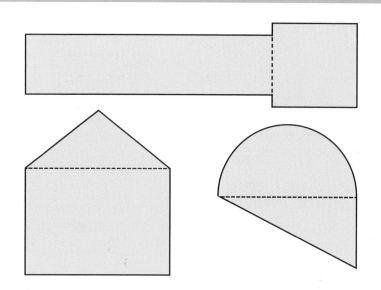

Examples

Find the areas of these compound shapes:

1

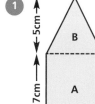

Area A = 7 x 4   = 28cm²
Area B = ½ x 4 x 5 = + 10cm²
Total Area   = 38cm²

2

Divide the shape into two rectangles

Area A = 6 x 2 = 12cm²
Area B = 3 x 3 = + 9cm²
Total Area   = 21cm²

3

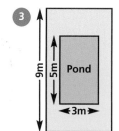

To work out the area of the path around this pond, work out the area of the two rectangles, then subtract the smaller area from the larger one.

Outer Area = 9 x 5 =   45m²
Area Pond = 5 x 3 = – 15m²
Area of Path   =   30m²

4

The two semi-circles together make one circle with radius 1.5cm (not 3cm!)

Area of...
Circle = 3.14 x 1.5² =   7.07cm²
Rectangle = 5 x 3 = +   15cm²
Total Area   = 22.07cm²

❓ Now try these...

1 Find the areas of these compound shapes.

a)

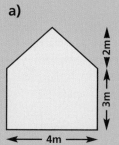

b)

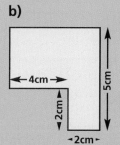

c)

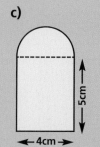

d)

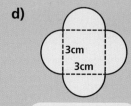

What do the four semi-circles make when added together?

e)

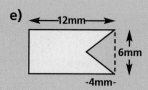

The triangle has been cut out, so subtract it!

Area

Examples

Calculate the missing lengths in these shapes.

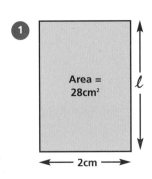

1

Area =
28cm²

ℓ

2cm

$\ell \times w = \textbf{Area}$
$\ell \times 2 = 28$
$\dfrac{\ell \times \cancel{2}}{\cancel{2}} = \dfrac{28}{2}$
$\ell = \textbf{14cm}$

This is just like solving
a linear equation in
algebra (see p.40)

2

Area =
36cm²

ℓ

ℓ

$\ell \times \ell = \textbf{Area}$
$\ell^2 = 36$
$\sqrt{\ell^2} = \sqrt{36}$
$\ell = \textbf{6cm}$

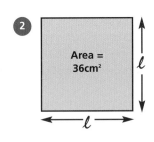

3

r

Area =
78.5cm²

$\pi \times r^2 = \textbf{Area}$
$3.14 \times r^2 = 78.5$
$\dfrac{3.14 \times r^2}{3.14} = \dfrac{78.5}{3.14}$
$r^2 = 25$
$r = \sqrt{25}$
$r = \textbf{5cm}$

(i) You need to know...

- **how to find an unknown side length in a shape using its area measurement.**

For shapes like rectangles and circles, where there is a standard formula for finding the area, it is also possible to work backwards and use the area to find an unknown length measurement, e.g. the width/length of a rectangle or the radius of a circle.

? Now try these...

Find the missing lengths in these shapes.

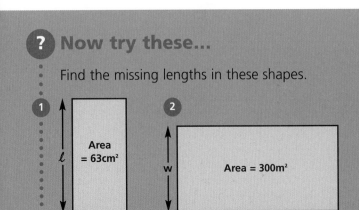

1

ℓ

Area
= 63cm²

7cm

2

w

Area = 300m²

20m

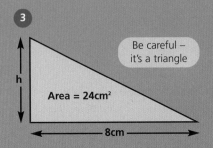

3

h

Area = 24cm²

8cm

Be careful –
it's a triangle

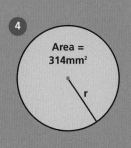

4

Area =
314mm²

r

LEVEL 5/6

✓ You should already know...

- that the words 'face', 'edge' and 'vertex' (or corner) are used to describe 3-D solids
- that a net is a 2-D plan or pattern that is cut and folded to make a 3-D solid.

ⓘ You also need to know...

- how to use common 2-D representations of 3-D solids.

Isometric paper can be used to draw 3-D solids. Isometric paper consists of dots or a grid arranged in equilateral triangles.

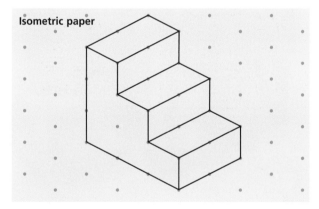

Isometric paper

Plans and elevations show what a 3-D solid looks like from different viewpoints.

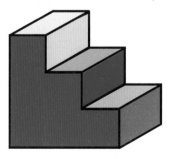

A plan shows what the solid looks like from above. Elevations show what it looks like from the front and the side.

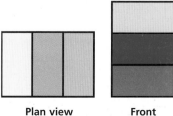

| Plan view | Front elevation | Side elevation |

A cross-section drawing shows what a 3-D solid would look like if you sliced through it.

A **prism** is a 3-D solid with a uniform cross-section. That means its cross-section is exactly the same all the way through.

Cylinder

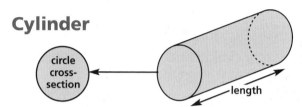

circle cross-section

length

Triangular prism

(You can also have pentagonal, hexagonal, octagonal, etc. prisms)

triangle cross-section

Cone

A cone is not a prism because it gets smaller towards the top.

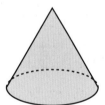

Sphere

A sphere is definitely not a prism!

? Now try these...

1. Draw the plan view, front elevation and side elevation of this solid.

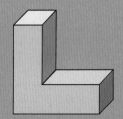

2. Draw the net of a cylinder.

✓ You should already know...

- that the volume of a cuboid can be found by counting the total number of cubes that fit into it
- that volume is measured in cubic units, e.g. cm³.

ⓘ You also need to know...

- the formula for finding the volume of a cuboid and how to use it.

The formula for the volume of a cube is

$V = \ell \times \ell \times \ell$

or

$V = \ell^3$.

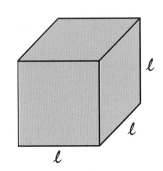

The formula for the volume of a cuboid is

$V = \ell \times w \times h$.

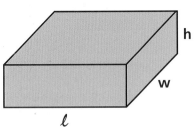

Examples

① Find the volume of this cuboid.

$V = \ell \times w \times h$
$V = 3 \times 7 \times 3$
$V = 63cm^3$

3cm
7cm
3cm

② Find the volume of this cube.

$V = \ell^3$
$V = 4.5^3$
(or $4.5 \times 4.5 \times 4.5$)
$V = 91.125cm^3$

4.5cm
4.5cm
4.5cm

❓ Now try these...

① Find the volume of each of these cubes and cuboids.

a)
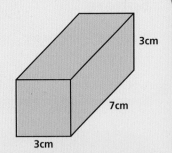
3cm
5cm
4cm

b)
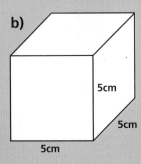
5cm
5cm
5cm

c)
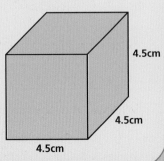
6cm
2cm
3cm

② What is the volume of a box measuring 15cm by 5cm by 10cm?

③ How many 1cm³ cubes could you fit inside a box 6cm long, 4cm wide and 3cm high?

Volume

Examples

1

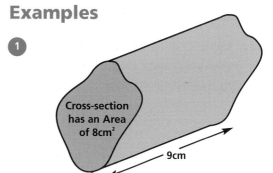

Cross-section has an Area of 8cm²

9cm

Volume of prism = Area of cross-section x ℓ
= 8cm² x 9cm
= 72cm³

2

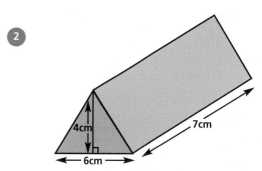

4cm

7cm

6cm

Area of triangle = $\frac{1}{2}$ x b x h
= $\frac{1}{2}$ x 6 x 4
= 12cm²

Volume of prism = Area of cross-section x ℓ
= 12cm² x 7cm
= 84cm³

3

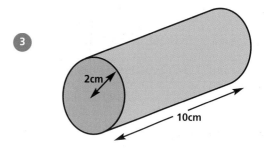

2cm

10cm

Area of circle = πr^2
= 3.14 x 2²
= 12.56cm²

Volume of prism = Area of cross-section x ℓ
= 12.56cm² x 10cm
= 125.6cm³

i You need to know...

- **how to calculate the volume of prisms.**

A **prism** is a 3-D solid, which has a **uniform cross-section**. That means, the cross-section remains exactly the same for the entire length of the prism.

Therefore, if you multiply the area of the cross-section by the prism's length, you can find the volume of the prism.

Volume of prism = Area of cross-section x ℓ

? Now try these...

Find the volume of these prisms:

1

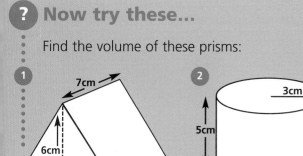

7cm

6cm

8cm

2

3cm

5cm

3

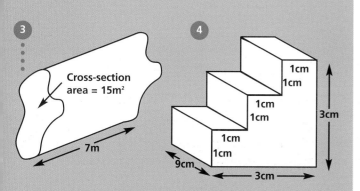

Cross-section area = 15m²

7m

4

1cm
1cm

1cm
1cm

3cm

1cm
1cm

9cm

3cm

Dimensions

ℹ️ You need to know...

- **how to distinguish between formulae for perimeter, area and volume by considering dimensions.**

It is possible to tell whether a formula is for volume, area or length by looking at dimensions. A dimension is a length and is represented by a letter in a formula.

If there is only one letter in the formula it represents a length, e.g. ℓ, **r, d.**

If 2 letters are multiplied together, the formula represents an area, e.g. **bh, r², $\dfrac{ab}{2}$**.

Formulae for volume have 3 letters multiplied together, e.g. **lwb, r³, $\dfrac{cde}{4}$** .

It doesn't matter if numbers are in the formulae – they don't change the dimensions, only the value of the answer when the formula is used.

Sometimes several formulae are combined together by adding or subtracting – in this case every term has to be of the same dimension for the formula to be correct.

Examples

What do the following formulae represent?

1. $\frac{1}{2}ab - \ell^2$ **2-D (area) formula**

2. $4(x + y)$ **1-D (length) formula**

3. $\pi r^2 h - abc$ **3-D (volume) formula**

❓ Now try these...

For each formula state whether it could be used to find a length, an area, a volume. Some are not correct. Which ones are they?

1. $ab - cd$

2. $\pi r^2 + \ell^2$

3. $r(r + 4h)$

4. $\dfrac{x^2}{y}$

5. $r^2 - 3$

6. $4(a - b)h$

     Hint: think about a trapezium

7. $xyz - r^2h + 2w^3$

8. $\dfrac{5(a + b + c)}{2}$

9. $2a^2 - 6 + r^2$

10. x^2y^2

11. x^2y^3

12. $\dfrac{rh}{4}$

Circles

ℹ You need to know...

- **the definition of a circle and the meaning of related terms**
- **that a tangent at any point on a circle is perpendicular to the radius at that point**
- **that the perpendicular from the centre to a chord bisects the chord.**

In maths, a circle is defined as the loci (line) of all the points that are an equal distance from the centre.

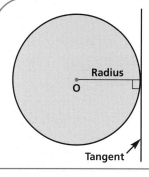

A **tangent** is a straight line which touches the circumference of a circle at one point. It always creates a right angle (i.e. it is **perpendicular**) with the radius at that point.

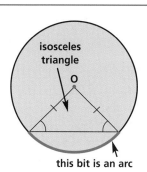

Look out for isosceles triangles in circles – the two sides of the triangle are radii and therefore equal.

An **arc** is any part of the **circumference**.

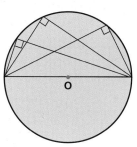

The angle of a triangle drawn inside a semi-circle is always a right angle.

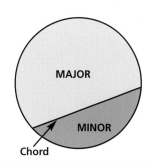

A **chord** is a line that goes from one side of a circle to the other but does not pass through the centre.

Segments are formed by a chord. They can be major or minor.

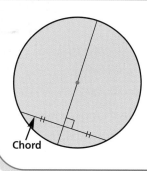

A line drawn through the centre of a circle so that it crosses a chord at right-angles will **bisect** the chord i.e. it will cut the chord into two halves of exact equal length.

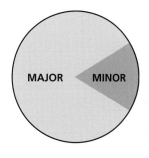

A **sector** is the area enclosed by two radii and an arc. It can be major or minor.

? Now try these...

1. Write down the part of the circle that each label is pointing to in the diagram.

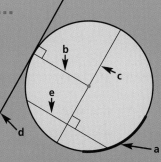

2. Chord AB is 10cm long. What is the length of line section AD?

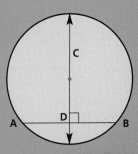

You need to know...

- **how to understand and use Pythagoras' Theorem.**

Pythagoras' Theorem can be used to calculate the length of a side of a right-angled triangle, providing the lengths of the other two sides are known.

Pythagoras' Theorem states... 'the square on the hypotenuse of a right-angled triangle is equal to the sum of the squares on the other two sides'.

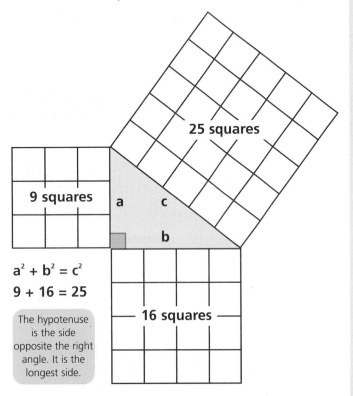

$$a^2 + b^2 = c^2$$
$$9 + 16 = 25$$

> The hypotenuse is the side opposite the right angle. It is the longest side.

Examples

1 Calculate the length of **c** in the right-angled triangle to 1 decimal place.

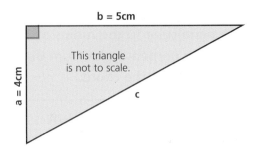

This triangle is not to scale.

Using Pythagoras' Theorem
$$c^2 = a^2 + b^2$$
$$c^2 = 4^2 + 5^2$$
$$c^2 = 16 + 25$$
$$c^2 = 41$$
$$c = \sqrt{41}$$

> To get **c**, take the square root.

$c = \textbf{6.4cm}$ (remember the units)

2 Calculate the height of this isosceles triangle to 3 significant figures.

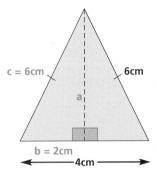

First we must divide the triangle into two right-angled triangles (as shown by the dotted line) in order to use Pythagoras' Theorem and label the one we are going to work with (in red).

$$c^2 = a^2 + b^2$$

> This would be true for both of the right-angled triangles

$$a^2 = c^2 - b^2$$

> rearrange the formula to make a^2 the subject

$$a^2 = 6^2 - 2^2$$
$$a^2 = 36 - 4$$
$$a^2 = 32$$
$$a = \sqrt{32}$$

> To get **a**, take the square root.

$a = \textbf{5.66cm}$ (remember the units)

❓ Now try these...

Calculate the lengths of the sides marked x.

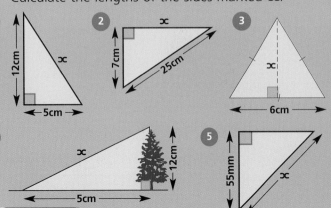

Trigonometry

You need to know...

- **how to use trigonometry to solve problems.**

The three trigonometrical ratios **sine (sin)**, **cosine (cos)** and **tangent (tan)** can only be used with right-angled triangles.

The ratios can be used to find an unknown side length when you have the measurements for one side and an angle or to find an unknown angle when you have measurements for two sides.

The three ratios can be put in formula triangles:

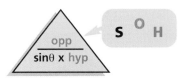

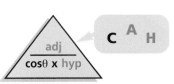

> This forms the name of a native American chief **'SOH CAH TOA'**. Remember this and you'll never confuse these ratios.

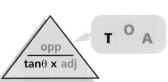

Where **H** is the **Hypotenuse** (see opposite page), **O** is the side **Opposite** the angle you are working with and **A** is the remaining side, **Adjacent** to (next to) the angle.

Now try these...

1. Calculate the lengths of the sides marked x.

   a)   b)   c)

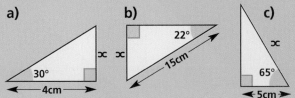

2. Calculate the angles marked θ.

   a)   b)   c)

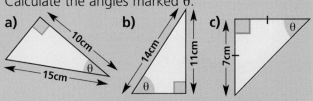

Examples

① Calculate the length of BC.

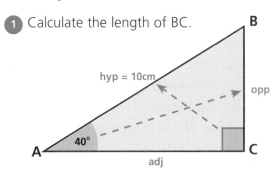

You have the **hypotenuse** and need to find the **opposite**, so use **sin (SOH)**

$$opp = \sin\theta \times hyp$$
$$BC = \sin 40° \times 10cm$$
$$BC = 0.643 \times 10cm$$
$$BC = 6.4cm \text{ (to 1 d.p.)}$$

② Calculate the size of angle BÂC.

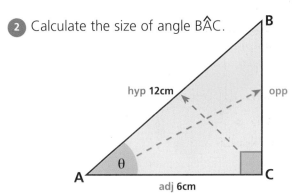

Since you have the Adjacent and Hypotenuse, you need to use **cos (CAH)**.

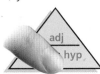

$$\cos\theta = \frac{adj}{hyp}$$

$$\cos B\hat{A}C = \frac{6cm}{12cm}$$

$$\cos B\hat{A}C = 0.5$$
$$B\hat{A}C = \cos^{-1}0.5$$
$$B\hat{A}C = 60°$$

> To calculate **BÂC** we now have to use the **inverse cos** button on our calculator, i.e. the **cos⁻¹** button to get the answer

You should already know...

- that a 2-D shape has reflective symmetry if one side of the shape is a perfect mirror image of the other
- that a 2-D shape has rotational symmetry, if you can rotate the shape into different positions and it looks the same as it did to start with.

 ## You also need to know...

- how to recognise and visualise plane symmetry in 3-D solids.

3-D solids have plane symmetry if they can be cut into two identical pieces that are mirror images of each other. The line of the cut through the shape is called the plane of symmetry. The examples below show one plane of symmetry for each shape but there are more.

Example

How many planes of symmetry does this prism have? Draw them in.

It has 2 planes of symmetry.

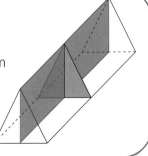

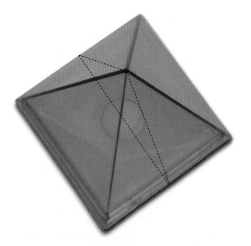  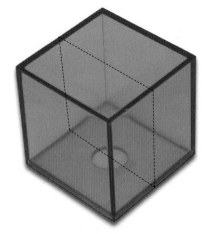

? Now try these...

1 A cube has lots of planes of symmetry. One is shown on this page. Can you draw another?

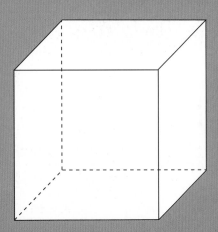

2 A cylinder has lots of planes of symmetry. Draw two.

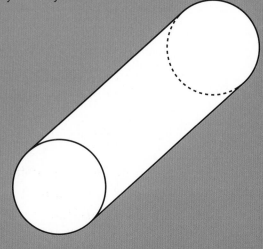

Transformations

ℹ You need to know...

- **how to identify and describe the mirror line of a reflected object.**

Here are some common lines that you should know, A line with the equation **x = 'a number'** is a vertical line through that number on the x-axis.

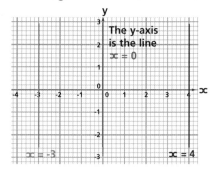

A line with the equation **y = 'a number'** is a horizontal line through that number on the y-axis.

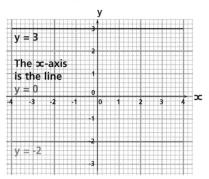

The line **y = x** is the diagonal line where the numbers in the coordinates are the same, i.e. it goes through (-1,-1), (2,2), (5,5), etc.

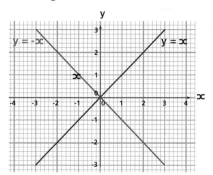

The other diagonal is **y = -x** (see p.58). In this case, although the numerical values of the x and y coordinates are the same, one will have a minus sign (except for when it goes through (0,0)!), i.e. it goes through (-3,3), (-4,4), (2,-2) etc.

Examples

① Reflect the shape in the line y = 0. Label the image A.

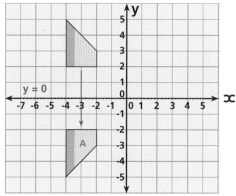

② Reflect the shape in the line y = x. Label the image B.

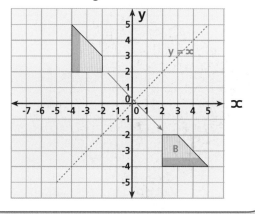

❓ Now try these...

① Reflect the shape in the following lines of reflection:

a) y = 1. Label the image A.

b) y = -x. Label the image B.

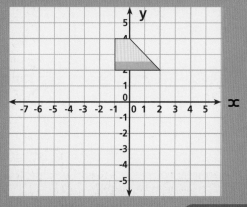

You need to know...

- **how to rotate objects about a given centre of rotation.**

Rotations can be performed on graph paper using axes. You need to specify the angle and direction of the rotation, and the centre of rotation is given by coordinates. Use tracing paper to help.

1

To rotate triangle A 90° clockwise about the centre (-1,1), carefully trace the axes and shape on the tracing paper.

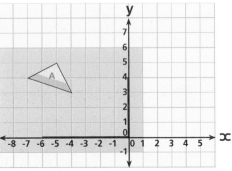

2

Place the point of your compass on the centre of rotation (-1,1) and rotate the paper clockwise.

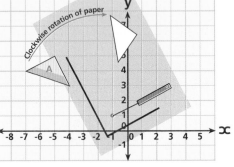

3

After 90° rotation, use the tracing paper as a guide and mark each corner of the shape on the graph paper.

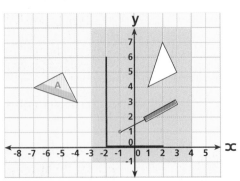

4

Remove the tracing paper and draw in the edges to complete the image.

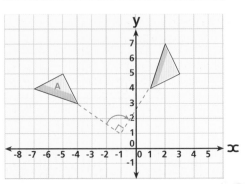

Example

Rotate the triangle ...

a) 90° clockwise about (0,0). Label it A.

b) 180° about (-1,1). Label it B.

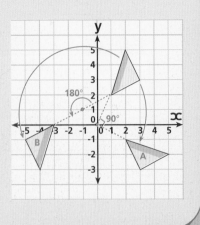

? Now try these...

1 Rotate triangle A ...

a) 90° anti-clockwise around (0,0). Label it B.

b) 180° around (0,-3). Label it C.

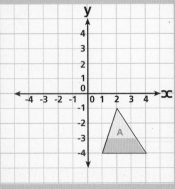

Transformations

You need to know...

- **how to describe and perform a translation using a distance and a direction.**

A translation is where you 'slide' an object into a new position. The size and shape of the object remain exactly the same, so the translated image is always congruent to the original shape. To describe a translation you must specify the direction and the distance the shape is being moved. However, instead of saying 'two to the right and three up', you use a vector.

$$\begin{pmatrix} x \\ y \end{pmatrix}$$

the **x** number tells us how many units to move horizontally. Movement to the right (→) is positive, left (←) is negative.

the **y** number tells us how many units to move vertically. Movement up (↑) is positive, down (↓) is negative.

Examples

1 Translate shape A by vector $\begin{pmatrix} 4 \\ 0 \end{pmatrix}$

(4 squares to the right).

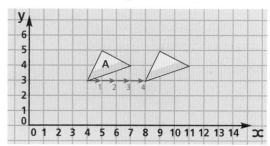

2 Translate shape B by vector $\begin{pmatrix} -1 \\ -2 \end{pmatrix}$

(1 square to the left and 2 squares down).

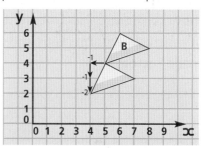

Now try these...

1

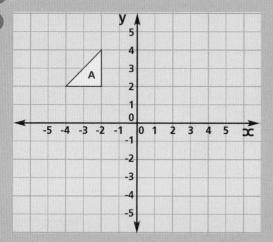

a) Translate triangle A by vector $\begin{pmatrix} 5 \\ 1 \end{pmatrix}$. Label it B.

b) Translate triangle A by vector $\begin{pmatrix} 0 \\ -3 \end{pmatrix}$. Label it C.

c) Describe the translation from B to C.

2

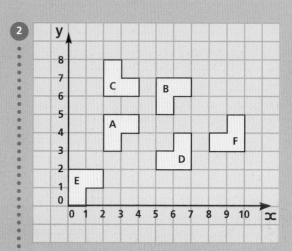

Which of these are translations?
a) A to B   **b)** C to D   **c)** A to E
d) B to D   **e)** E to B   **f)** D to F
Give the vectors for those which are.

Reprints and enlargement
gifts for the family and fr

print si
6" x 4'

A

B

C

You need to know...

- **how to visualise and recognise enlargements of shapes**
- **how to produce enlargements specified by a centre of enlargement and a positive scale factor.**

An **enlargement** changes the size of a shape, but the ratio of the sides stays the same. To describe an enlargement you need to give the centre of enlargement and the scale factor. The length of each of the shape's sides is multiplied by the scale factor to give the side lengths for the enlarged image.

Examples

1 Enlarge shape A by scale factor 2. The centre of enlargement is (0,0).

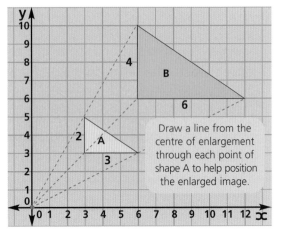

Draw a line from the centre of enlargement through each point of shape A to help position the enlarged image.

2 Enlarge shape A by scale factor 3. The centre of enlargement is (3,1).

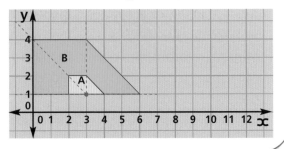

Now try these...

1

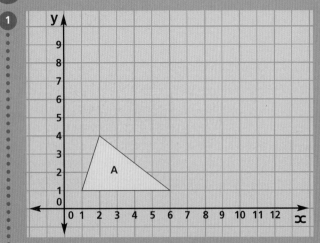

Enlarge triangle A by scale factor 2 using the origin (0,0) as the centre of enlargement. Label your image B.

2

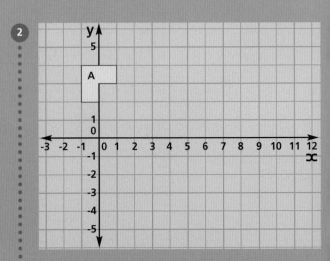

Enlarge shape A by scale factor 3 using (-3,5) as the centre of enlargement. Label your image B.

Transformations

ℹ You need to know...

- **how to enlarge objects by a fractional scale factor.**

Enlargements by fractional scale factors actually result in a reduction in size. Look again at the examples on p.96. In Example 1 shape B is an enlargement by scale factor 2 of shape A with centre (0,0). We can also say that shape A is an enlargement by scale factor $\frac{1}{2}$ of shape B with centre (0,0).

In Example 2 on p.96 shape B is an enlargement of shape A by scale factor 3 with centre (3,1). We can also say that shape A is an enlargement of shape B by scale factor $\frac{1}{3}$, centre (3,1).

To calculate the coordinates for the points of the enlargement, all you need to do is count how many squares there are across and up from the centre of enlargement to each of the points on the original shape, then multiply by the scale factor.

? Now try these...

1. Enlarge quadrilateral ABCD by scale factor $\frac{1}{2}$ using centre (7,1). Label the image A'B'C'D'.

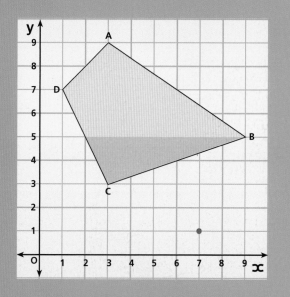

Example

a) Enlarge shape A by scale factor $\frac{1}{2}$, centre (5,1). Label the image B.

> In this example, point **a** is 2 squares to the left **(-2)**, and 8 squares up **(+8)** from the centre of enlargement (5,1). If you multiply these values by $\frac{1}{2}$, you will find that point **a'** will be 1 to the left **(-1)** and 4 squares up **(+4)** from the centre. Adding these values to the co-ordinates of the centre gives the new point as **(5-1,1+4) = (4,5)**. Check the other points in the same way.

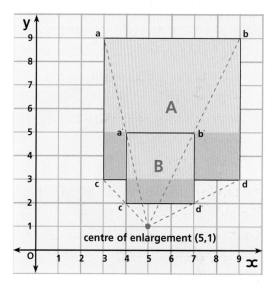

b) Enlarge shape A by scale factor $\frac{1}{3}$, centre (9,9). Label this image C.

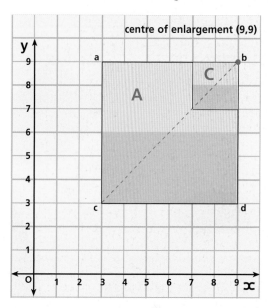

You need to know...

- **how to recognise similar shapes.**

Shapes are similar if they are exactly the same shape, but one is an enlargement of the other. The angles are the same but the side lengths are all increased by the same scale factor (see p.96).

Any two circles are mathematically similar, as are any two squares because all four sides are always equal and each interior angle will always be 90°. Two rectangles are not necessarily similar because the ratio of their side lengths (width to length) can vary.

Example

Which of these shapes are similar to A?

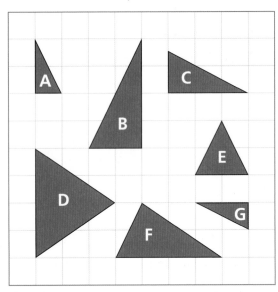

Shape B is similar to A. It is enlarged by a scale factor of 2 and reflected.
Shape C is similar to A. It is enlarged by a scale factor of $1\frac{1}{2}$, rotated and reflected.
Shape G is congruent to A. It is rotated and reflected.

? Now try these...

1. Which of these shapes are similar?

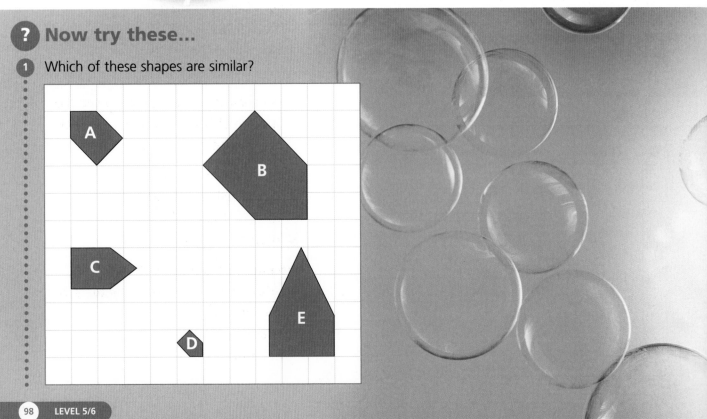

i You need to know...

- **how to calculate the area and volume of an enlarged object.**
- **that an enlarged object is similar to the original object.**

When a 2-D shape is enlarged, every length is multiplied by the scale factor...

Length of enlargement
= original length x scale factor

and the area is multiplied by the square of the scale factor...

Area of enlargement
= original area x scale factor squared

When a 3-D solid is enlarged, the length of each side and the area of each face are increased in the same way as for 2-D shapes. The volume is increased by the cube of the scale factor...

Volume of enlargement
= original volume x scale factor cubed

Whatever scale factor you enlarge an object by, the resulting enlargement will always be similar to the original because the proportions remain the same.

? Now try these...

1 A triangle with base 4cm and height 6cm is enlarged by scale factor 3. What is the new area of the enlargement?

2 What is the volume of a cuboid measuring 2mm x 3mm x 4mm? What will be the volume of the cuboid that has been enlarged by scale factor 2? (Don't just double the side lengths, use the rule above.)

3 What is the scale factor for this enlargement and what length is x?

 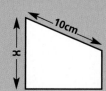

Example

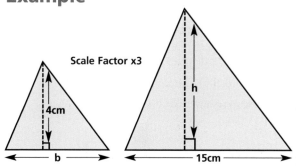

Scale Factor x3

a) Find the missing lengths (h and b).

h = 4 x 3
h = 12cm
$$b = \frac{15}{3}$$
b = 5cm

b) Calculate the area of the original shape.

$$A = \frac{1}{2} x\ 4\ x\ 5$$
A = 10cm²

c) Use the formula opposite to calculate the area of the enlarged shape.

Area of enlargement
= original area x SF²
= 10 x 3²
= 10 x 9 = 90cm²

d) If the original triangle is the cross-section of a prism of length 10cm, what will the volume of the enlarged prism be?

Volume of original prism
= cross-section x length
= 10cm² x 10cm
= 100cm³

Volume of Enlargement
= original volume x scale factor cubed
= 100cm³ x 3³
= 100cm³ x 27
= 2700cm³

Tessellation

- **how to recognise if a shape tessellates.**

If lots of examples of the same shape can be fitted together exactly, with no gaps, we say it tessellates. These shapes tessellate…

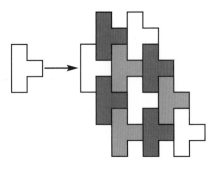

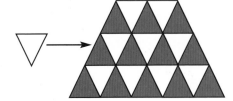

…but these won't…

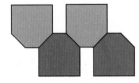 

Examples

1 Will this shape produce a tessellation?

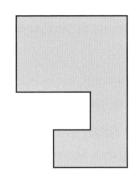 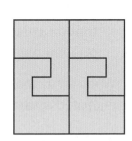

Yes.

2 Does this shape tessellate?

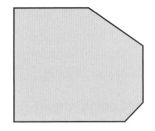 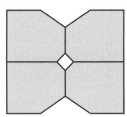

No. It leaves gaps.

❓ Now try these...

Try to produce a tessellation with each shape below and state whether it will or will not tessellate. Remember the shapes may fit together in more than one way.

a) **b)** **c)** **d)**

e) **f)** **g)** **h)**

Congruence

You need to know...

- **how to identify congruent triangles.**

Triangles are congruent if they can be mapped onto each other. To be congruent, they need to be identical in shape and size, but their position in relation to each other may be different. So if a triangle is rotated or reflected, the image will be congruent to the original.

There are four sets of conditions that can be used to identify congruent triangles:

1. Three matching sides (SSS)
2. Two matching sides and one matching angle (SAS)
3. Two matching angles and one matching side (ASA)
4. A matching right angle, hypotenuse and one other side (RHS)

The matching sides and angles must all be in the same positions in relation to each other.

Now try these...

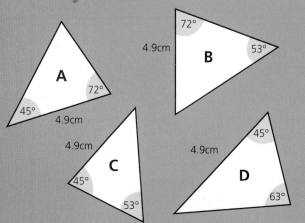

Here are four triangles (not drawn to scale).

a) Are triangles B and C congruent?

b) Are triangles A and D congruent?

Explain your answers.

Examples

Are the following pairs of triangles congruent?

1   AB = PQ
 BC = QR
 AC = PR
 ∴ ABC and PQR are congruent triangles.

> Three Sides, **SSS**.

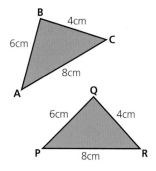

2   AB = PQ
 AC = PR
 Â = P̂
 ∴ ABC and PQR are congruent triangles.

> Two matching sides and one matching angle, **SAS**.

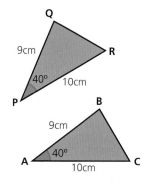

3   AB = PQ
 Â = P̂
 B̂ = Q̂
 ∴ ABC and PQR are congruent triangles.

> Two matching angles and one matching side, **ASA**.

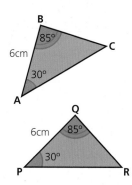

4   AB = PQ
 BC = QR
 Ĉ = R̂ = 90°
 ∴ ABC and PQR are congruent triangles.

> A matching right angle, hypotenuse and one other side, **RHS**.

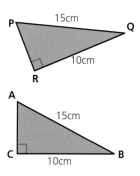

ⓘ You need to know...

- **how to construct angles of 60° and 90°**
- **how to construct a perpendicular from a point on a line**
- **how to construct the bisector of an angle.**

Construction of an Angle of 60° and 90°

Angle of 60°

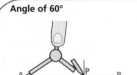  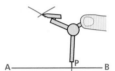 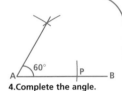

1. Draw an arc from A to cross AB at P

2. Draw another arc from A of same radius.

3. Draw arc from P (again same radius).

4. Complete the angle.

Angle of 90°

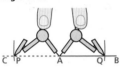 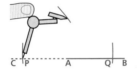 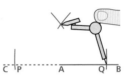 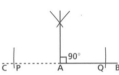

1. Extend A with a dotted line to C. Draw two arcs from A (same radius) to cross CB at P and Q.

2. Draw arc of longer radius from P. Mark above A.

3. Repeat from Q using arc of same radius.

4. Complete the angle.

The Perpendicular from a Point on a Line

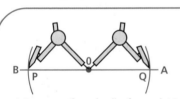 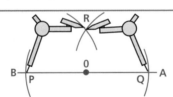 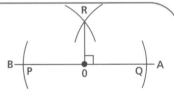

1. Draw arcs of equal radius from point 0, to cross AB at P and Q.

2. Draw arcs of the same radius (but greater than step 1) from P and Q to intersect at R.

3. Join 0 to R to form the perpendicular from point 0.

The Bisector of an Angle

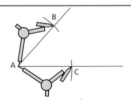 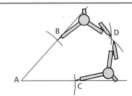 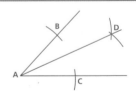

Draw arcs of equal radius from point A to cut lines at B and C.

Draw arcs of equal radius from points B and C to intersect at point D

Join A to D to form the bisector of the angle.

❓ Now try these...

Using the methods above, construct...

a) an angle of 90°

b) an angle of 60°

c) the perpendicular from a point on a line

d) the bisector of the 60° angle you created in **b)**

e) a square from the angle you made in **a)**

f) an equilateral triangle of side 7cm.

Constructions and Loci

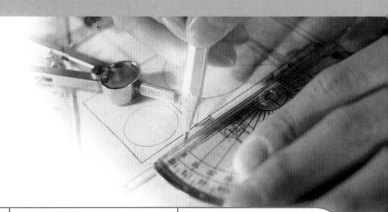

ℹ You need to know...

- **how to construct loci.**

A locus is a line, all the points of which follow a particular rule. The boxes below explain the rules for the loci and how to construct them.

The locus of all points at a constant distance from a fixed point is a **circle** whose radius is equal to the constant distance.

P

The locus of points which are always at a constant distance from a line is a **pair of parallel lines**, one each side of the line, with a **semi-circle** at each end of the line.

Q
P

The locus of points which are always equidistant from two points is a **line which bisects the two points at right angles** (i.e. a perpendicular bisector).

P ●─ ─ ─ ─ ┤├─ ─ ─ ─● Q

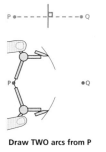

Draw TWO arcs from P

Draw TWO arcs from Q (same radius as from P)

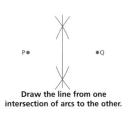

Draw the line from one intersection of arcs to the other.

The locus of points which are always equidistant from two lines is a **line which bisects the angle between the two lines** (i.e. an angle bisector).

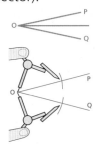

Draw TWO arcs from O to cross the lines OP and OQ

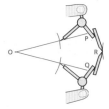

Draw TWO arcs from where the first two arcs cross the lines to form point R.

Draw the line from R to O to form the angle bisector.

❓ Now try these...

1 Line AB is 6cm. Construct the locus of points 5cm from line AB.

2 Construct the locus of points 4cm away from a fixed point, in a 30° section.

3 A goat is attached to a railing 10m long by a rope with a ring around the railing. The rope is 2m long. Using a scale of 1cm to 2m, construct and shade the region the goat can reach.

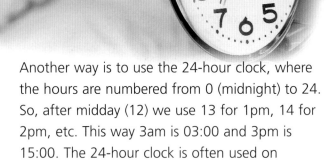

ⓘ You need to know...

- **how to use standard units of time.**

Here are the standard units used for measuring time. You will already be familiar with them, but make sure you learn all the equivalent values too.

60 seconds = 1 minute
60 minutes = 1 hour
24 hours = 1 day
7 days = 1 week
365 days =
52 weeks = } **1 year**
366 days = 1 leap year (extra day is 29th February)
10 years = 1 decade
100 years = 1 century
1000 years = 1 millennium

Time can be measured using 12-hour and 24-hour clocks. We tend to use the 12-hour clock when talking about time in our day-to-day lives.

This is a 12-hour clock. It shows 7 o'clock, but you don't know if it's in the morning or in the evening. We use 7am to mean before midday and 7pm to mean after midday to be sure.

Another way is to use the 24-hour clock, where the hours are numbered from 0 (midnight) to 24. So, after midday (12) we use 13 for 1pm, 14 for 2pm, etc. This way 3am is 03:00 and 3pm is 15:00. The 24-hour clock is often used on timetables and schedules.

Examples

① A CD has a playing time of 120 minutes. What is that in hours?

1 hour = 60 minutes
120 ÷ 60 minutes = 2 hours

② My digital watch says it is 20:20. What time is this using a 12-hour clock? (Don't forget am or pm!)

20 – 12 = 8. Because 20 is bigger than 12, we know that it is a pm time, and subtracting 12 gives the correct hour. The minutes remain the same.
So it is 8.20pm.

❓ Now try these...

① Daniel starts a new job for which the annual (i.e. yearly) salary is £10 400. He is paid weekly. How much will he receive each week?

② Alex is looking for a new job. She has seen two jobs advertised. Job A is offering £825 a month and Job B is offering £5.50 an hour.
a) If she works 35 hours a week in each job, calculate how much she would earn from each job in a year.
b) Which job has the higher salary?

③ Complete this table showing 12-hour and 24-hour clock times.

12-hour	8.30am	9.45pm			12.00am	
24-hour			13.05	22.40		12.00

④ Use the rhyme '30 days has September, April, June and November. All the rest have 31, except for February alone which has 28 days clear and 29 in each leap year' to help you work out how many days...
a) from 18 May to 13 June
b) from 17 August to 23 October
(Don't forget September!)

ℹ You need to know...

- **how to perform calculations involving time**
- **how to perform time calculations in which fractions of an hour need to be treated as fractions or decimals.**

We often measure time in fractions of an hour i.e. $\frac{1}{4}$ of an hour, $\frac{1}{2}$ an hour, $\frac{3}{4}$ of an hour. Remember, the whole is 1 hour (or 60 minutes) so...

$\frac{1}{4}$ **of an hour =**

$\frac{1}{4}$ x 60 = 15 minutes ⟶ $\frac{15}{60}$ = 0.25 hours

$\frac{1}{2}$ **an hour =**

$\frac{1}{2}$ x 60 = 30 minutes ⟶ $\frac{30}{60}$ = 0.5 hours

$\frac{3}{4}$ **of an hour =**

$\frac{3}{4}$ x 60 = 45 minutes ⟶ $\frac{45}{60}$ = 0.75 hours

Make sure you don't mistake times for decimals. For example, 7.20 represents 7 hours and 20 minutes *not* 7.2 hours (which would be 7 hours and 12 minutes)!

Examples

Crogglethwaite	0720	0840	1022	1245
Daisy Vale	0735	0855	1039	1300
Barrowby Wood	0747	-	1055	1312
Hathersedge	0752	0909	1103	1317

Look at this timetable. It shows 4 trains from Crogglethwaite to Hathersedge which pass through Daisy Vale and Barrowby Wood on the way. Notice one of the trains doesn't stop at Barrowby Wood.

1 How long does it take the first train to get from Crogglethwaite to Hathersedge?

It takes 07:52 – 07:20 = **32 minutes** (remember to subtract the minutes first, then do the hours)

2 I want to leave Daisy Vale and be in Hathersedge before midday. What is the last train I can catch and how long will the journey take?

The last train arrives in Hathersedge too late so I'll have to get the **10:39 from Daisy Vale**. It arrives in Hathersedge at 11:03. The journey takes **24 minutes**. (From 10:39 there are 21 minutes until 11:00 then add on the extra 3 minutes after 11:00.)

❓ Now try these...

1 a) Use the timetable above to work out all the journey times from Crogglethwaite to Hathersedge.

b) One train is much slower than the others. Which one is it?

2 Use the timetable above to answer this question. I have to get from Daisy Vale to Barrowby Wood and arrive before 11am. Which train should I catch, and how long will the journey take?

3 Caroline needs to go shopping. It takes 25 minutes to drive to the shops and 25 minutes to drive home again. It will take her $\frac{3}{4}$ of an hour to shop. How long will the entire trip take? Give your answer in hours to 2 d.p.

4 A coach leaves at 11.35am. The journey takes 2 hours and 50 minutes. At what time does it arrive at its destination? (Give your answer in 24-hour time).

✓ You should already know...

- **that data which can be counted in whole numbers is called discrete data.**
- **that primary data is collected by you and secondary data is collected by someone else.**

ℹ You also need to know...

- **how to collect continuous data.**

Data can be collected by observation (e.g. counting) or by carrying out a survey (e.g. asking other people for information).

Another method is to take measurements. Data collected this way is called **continuous data**.

Continuous data can take any value in a certain range. For example, if you were measuring the height of people in your class, you would get all sorts of results, not just whole numbers (e.g. 162.5cm, 160cm, 173.8cm…).

When you collect continuous data you must be consistent. For example, use the same measuring equipment, the same units and the same level of accuracy for each measurement – if you round one number to 2 decimal places, make sure you do the same with all of them!

You are likely to get a wide range of different results when collecting continuous data. Depending on what you are looking for, you can record each measurement individually or you can record in a group called a **class interval** (see p.108).

Examples

1 Marcus thinks that the boys in his class play sport more often than the girls. He conducts a survey to find out how many times a week each pupil in his class plays sport. What type of data is this?

He is asking the pupils to **count** how many times they play sport in a week. They will give answers like once, twice, three times etc. **This is discrete data**.

2 Marcus wants to know if there is a link between the amount of sport pupils do and their body weight. He weighs all the pupils in his class. What type of data is this?

Weight is a **measurement**. **This is continuous data**.

❓ Now try these...

1 For each of these examples, say whether it is an example of discrete or continuous data.

a) Recording how many trains stop at a station in 1 day.

b) Recording the length of time each train waits at a station.

c) Recording the height of a sunflower over a period of time as it grows from a seed.

d) Recording how many leaves each sunflower has when fully grown.

2 Look at question 1c). How would you ensure that the data collected was consistent? Give four ways

Collecting Data

ℹ You need to know...

- **how to specify a hypothesis and test it**
- **how to design a survey sheet or experiment taking account of bias.**

A **hypothesis** is a statement or theory, e.g. 'girls buy more magazines than boys'. To test a hypothesis you need to...

1. state the hypothesis
2. collect data related to the hypothesis
3. collate and analyse the data
4. use your findings to test if the hypothesis is true or false.

Questionnaires can be used collect data to test hypotheses. When designing questionnaires...

- make questions clear and concise
- allow for all possible answers
- make the questions relevant
- avoid bias in the questions
- include clear instructions.

Bias will occur if you let your opinions influence other people's answers. It can also arise if a survey includes a large number of individuals from the same group (e.g. age group or culture) as they are likely to have similar ideas. To provide unbiased data, a survey needs to include a cross-section of the population.

Examples

1. A new spot cream needs to be tested. A shop manager gave samples to his sons to test. Why is this method biased?

   The sample is too small, only boys are testing the cream and we don't know if they have spots!

2. In a survey about people's reading habits, the following questions were asked:

   local questionnaire
   1. Do you agree that this town's daily paper is a complete waste of money?
   2. If you buy a newspaper, state which one and whether you buy it daily or only at weekends and if not, how do you normally keep up with political news?

a) Why are the questions unsatisfactory?

   Q1 is biased. It suggests that the answer is yes. Q2 is too long and is confusing because it asks more than one question.

b) Write questions to replace them.

   1. **The local daily paper is value for money.**
      Strongly agree ☐ Agree ☐
      Don't Know ☐ Disagree ☐
      Strongly Disagree ☐
   2. **Do you buy a newspaper?**
      Yes ☐ No ☐
      If your answer to Q2 was yes please answer Q3. If your answer to Q2 was no please answer Q4.
   3. **When do you buy a newspaper?**
      Daily ☐ Weekends only ☐
   4. **How do you keep up with political news?**
      Radio ☐ TV ☐ Other ☐

❓ Now try these...

1. Barry wanted to know people's opinions on fast foods. He gave the following questionnaire to 20 pupils in his maths class.

   fast food SURVEY
   Name ....
   Class ....
   1. Do you eat fast foods?
   2. What type of fast food do you eat?
   3. Don't you wish that your parents would buy fast food more often?
   4. I still think that fish and chips are the best don't you?

   a) Why is the sample biased?
   b) What could Barry have done to make the sample more representative of the school?
   c) Re-write the questions to make them more suitable.

Recording Data

✓ You should already know...

- **that discrete data can be recorded in a frequency table or tally chart.**

ⓘ You also need to know...

- **how to design and use two-way tables**
- **how to record continuous data in a frequency table using appropriate class intervals.**

Two-way tables are a simple way to record two sets of related information. They allow you to examine the information, find out more and fill in missing information, which can be very useful.

Continuous data can be recorded in a **grouped frequency table** with suitable **class intervals**. Class intervals are groups of equal width with no overlap. They are either written as open intervals in the form 1-, 10-, etc. (look at the table in Example 1) or as inequalities in the form $1 \leqslant h < 10$, $10 \leqslant h < 20$, etc. The size of each class interval will depend on the range of the data. You should always have fewer than 10 groups.

Examples

1. The heights of a group of 25 children were recorded to the nearest centimetre:
135, 120, 140, 134, 128, 141, 149, 156, 139, 152, 142, 153, 152, 120, 127, 129, 147, 139, 154, 148, 155, 143, 137, 129, 152
Draw a tally chart to represent the data.

> The range of heights is **156 – 120 = 36cm**. Choose four class intervals of width 10cm.

Height (cm)	Tally	Frequency
120-	卌 |	6
130-	卌	5
140-	卌 ||	7
150-	卌 ||	7
	Total	25

2. A survey of whether 240 Year 8 and Year 9 students used the school library during the lunch break or after school showed that 20 out of 100 Year 8 students used the library after school whilst a total of 160 students used the library at lunchtime. Create a two-way table, insert the data you have been given and fill in the missing information.

	Year 8	Year 9	Total
Lunchtime	80	80	160
After school	20	60	80
Total	100	140	240

? Now try these...

1. The temperature (in °C), in different cities throughout the world was recorded on one day:
31, 9, 12, 24, 17, 6, 19, 11, 21, 33, 13, 17, 5, 36, 22, 7, 14, 25, 9, 18, 4, 21, 28, 2, 10, 27, 12, 17, 19, 17
Draw a frequency table for the data, using suitable class intervals.

2. Two local secondary schools have a total of 3125 students. North Park has 1875 students of which 968 are boys, whilst South Street has only 549 boys. Draw a two-way table, enter the data you have and calculate the missing numbers.

Displaying Data

ℹ You need to know...

- **how to draw and interpret data in simple pie charts.**

Pie charts are circular graphs. The circle is divided into sectors and the size of each sector represents the frequency. To draw a pie chart from a table of results you need to work out the angle for each sector. Then you can mark out the angles using a protractor.

Here are the results of a survey of the pets that 24 pupils had. Cat - 6, Rabbit - 4, Bird - 2, Dog - 9, Hamster - 3.

Divide each number by the total number (to find the fraction) and multiply by 360° to find the angle for each sector.

Cat	6	$\frac{6}{24}$ x 360° = 90°
Rabbit	4	$\frac{4}{24}$ x 360° = 60°
Bird	2	$\frac{2}{24}$ x 360° = 30°
Dog	9	$\frac{9}{24}$ x 360° = 135°
Hamster	3	$\frac{3}{24}$ x 360° = 45°

Measure and mark 90° for cat	Measure and mark the angles for rabbit, bird and dog	Check that the remainder (for hamster) is 45°

 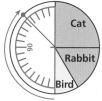 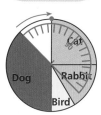

Always use a protractor when measuring angles and make sure you start reading the scale from 0°.

Each sector of the pie chart represents the number of children who have that animal as a pet. For example, you can clearly see that $\frac{1}{4}$ of the pupils have cats and that the most popular pet is a dog.

Example

300 pupils were asked what they do for lunch at school.

a) Copy and complete the table.

School canteen	165	$\frac{165}{300}$ x 360° = 198°
Packed lunch	75	$\frac{75}{300}$ x 360° = 90°
Go home	60	$\frac{60}{300}$ x 360° = 72°

b) Draw a pie chart for this information.

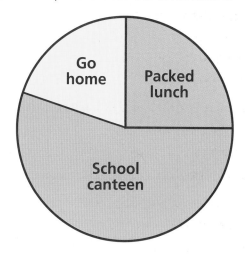

c) What proportion of pupils bring a packed lunch?

The slice for packed lunch is $\frac{1}{4}$ of the pie chart so $\frac{1}{4}$ or 25% of the pupils bring a packed lunch.

❓ Now try these...

1. Pupils were asked what their favourite snack was. Here are the results: fruit - 15, crisps - 100, chocolate - 165, ice cream - 50, cakes - 70.

   a) Put the information into a table and draw a pie chart.

   b) What was the least popular snack?

   c) What fraction of the pupils chose crisps as their favourite snack?

ℹ️ You need to know...

- **how to use bar charts to compare two or more sets of data**
- **how to interpret graphs and diagrams and draw conclusions.**

When two or more sets of data have a connection **comparative** or **compound bar charts** can be drawn so that you can compare and interpret the data.

This graph allows you to compare individual results.

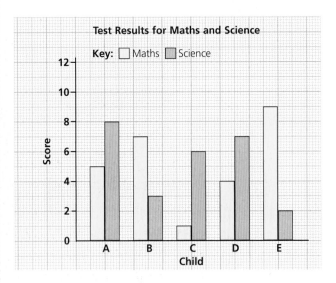

This compound bar chart allows you to compare the totals of both results.

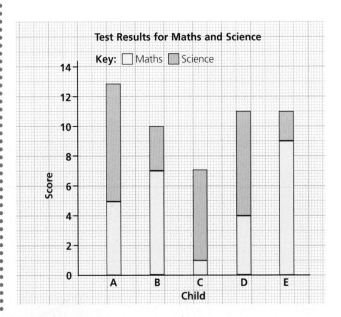

Examples

1 The bar chart shows the number of different coins in Joe's money box.

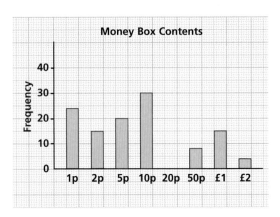

a) Which coin does he have exactly 20 of?

The only bar which shows a frequency of exactly 20 is the 5p column.

b) What is the total value of the 2p coins?

The 2p column reaches halfway between 10 and 20 on the frequency axis giving a frequency of 15.
Total value of 2p coins = 2 x 15 = 30p.

c) How many coins worth less than 5p does he have?

The only coins worth less than 5p are 1p and 2p. From the graph we can see that there are 24 1p coins and 15 2p coins **so the answer is 24 + 15 = 39 coins**.

d) What is the total value of the coins worth 50p or more?

The coins worth 50p or more are:
50p coin with a frequency of 8,
value = 50 x 8 = £4
£1 coin with a frequency of 15,
value = 15 x 1 = £15
£2 coin with a frequency of 4,
value = 2 x 4 = £8.
The total value is 4 + 15 + 8 = £27.

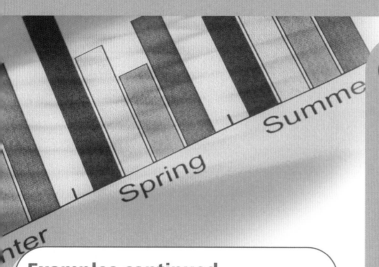

Examples continued

2 The number of people over 17 and the number of people owning a driving licence in a particular street were noted over a period of years. These are shown in the table below.

Year	1970	1975	1980	1985	1990	1995
Over 17	32	27	29	31	33	31
Driving licence	12	17	19	20	24	28

a) Represent this data in a comparative bar chart.

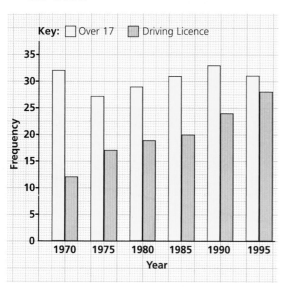

b) Compare and comment on the results.

The graph shows that whilst the number of people over 17 has remained constant over the period the number of people owning a driving licence has increased.

? ## Now try these...

1 A school is raising money for a new minibus. It needs to raise £15 000. The bar chart shows the amount of money raised:

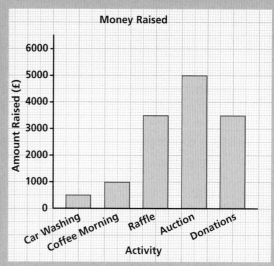

a) How much have they raised so far?

b) Which activities raised the same amount of money?

2 The results of a survey on methods of transport used by students to get to school in summer and winter are displayed in a bar chart:

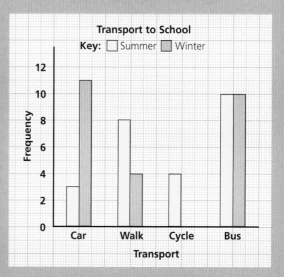

a) How many students took part in the survey?

b) How many students walk to school in summer?

c) Which method of transport was used by the same number of people in the summer and winter?

You should already know...

- **that discrete data can be displayed in bar charts and pictograms**
- **that line graphs can be used to show a pattern of change over time.**

You also need to know...

- **how to construct and interpret frequency diagrams for grouped continuous data.**

Continuous data can be shown in a line graph. If it is grouped, however, you will need to draw a **frequency diagram**.

There are two types of frequency diagram. One uses bars to represent the data. The other uses lines and is called a **frequency polygon**.

The easiest way to draw a frequency polygon is to start by constructing a frequency diagram using bars. In a frequency diagram there are no gaps between the bars.

You then need to mark the **midpoint** at the top of each bar with a small cross or dot. Finally, join all the points using straight lines.

Example

The heights of 25 children are shown in the table:

Height (cm)	Frequency
120-	6
130-	4
140-	8
150-	7

a) Draw a frequency diagram to show this data.

> Remember, the class intervals need to be the same width for your diagram to make sense.

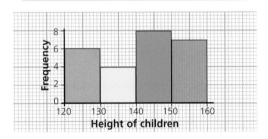

b) Draw a frequency polygon to show this data.

> Use your frequency diagram as a starting point. Your crosses/dots must be exactly in the middle of each class interval.

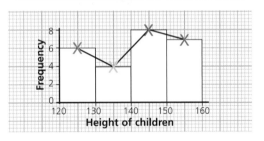

Now try these...

1 The table shows the weights of 25 new members who joined a gym in January:

Weight	Frequency
50<w≤70	5
70<w≤90	8
90<w≤110	7
110<w≤130	4
130<w<150	1

a) Draw a frequency diagram to show this data.
b) Draw a frequency polygon to show this data.
c) How many new gym members weighed between 90kg and 130kg?
d) How many new gym members weighed under 110kg?

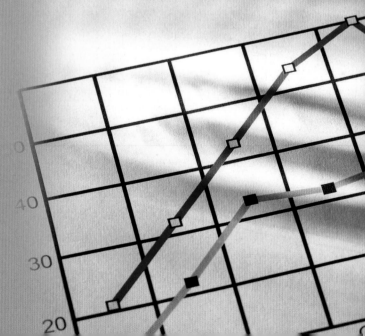

Displaying Data

ℹ You need to know...

- **how to construct frequency polygons.**

As shown on the facing page, **frequency polygons** are a set of points joined up with straight lines. They can only be used with class intervals of equal width. They show the trend of a set of data and can be used to compare two sets of data. Frequency polygons can also be drawn by plotting the points **straight onto the axes**. The points are found by plotting the midpoint of each class interval against frequency.

Example

The exam results for two schools are recorded in the frequency table opposite.

Mark	0-	10-	20-	30-	40-	50-	60-	70-	80-	90-
School A	4	10	8	12	18	16	14	9	3	2
School B	0	0	6	10	16	22	12	11	10	5

a) Draw a frequency polygon to represent this data. Plot the points for each school (e.g. School A: (5,4), (15,10), etc. Where the first coordinate is the midpoint of the class interval and the second coordinate is the frequency.

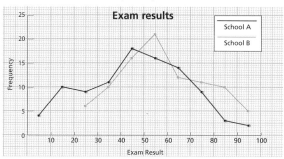

b) Comment on the results.

The results for School B are generally higher than School A. (School B's frequency polygon is generally above and to the right of School A's, showing higher frequencies for the higher marks.)

School A's marks are more spread out than school B's. (This is shown by the width of each polygon.)

❓ Now try these...

1 Fifty males and fifty females were interviewed about the way they spend their income. The percentage income saved by each group is shown in the table below.

% Saved	0-	10-	20-	30-	40-	50-	60-70
Males	2	0	19	10	11	8	0
Females	3	3	14	12	9	6	3

a) Draw a frequency polygon for each distribution on the same axes.

b) Comment on the graphs.

2 The frequency polygon shows the number of electrical goods sold by two shop assistants over a 10 week period. Use the polygon to answer the questions below.

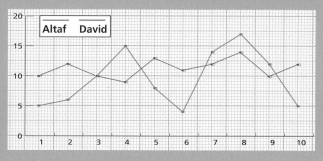

a) "It is easy to predict Altaf's sales in week 11." Explain why this statement is true.

b) "David is the better salesman." Comment on this statement.

You need to know...

- **how to draw scatter diagrams and understand correlation.**

A **scatter diagram** is a graph with two sets of data plotted against each other. If there is a relationship between the two sets of data, **correlation** occurs.

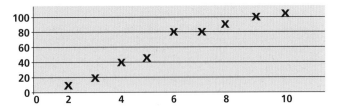

This diagram shows a **positive correlation**. As one variable increases so does the other one.

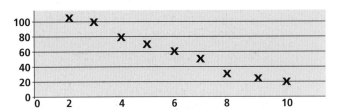

This diagram shows a **negative correlation**. As one variable increases the other one decreases.

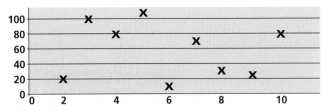

This diagram shows **no correlation**. There is no obvious relationship between the two sets of data.

Example

An experiment was carried out to measure the height to which a rubber ball bounced after being dropped from various heights.

Height of drop (cm)	50	75	100	125	150	175	200
Height of bounce (cm)	20	25	50	60	75	75	100

a) Draw a scatter diagram for the data.
To draw a scatter diagram you plot pairs of numbers onto the graph in the same way as you plot coordinates.

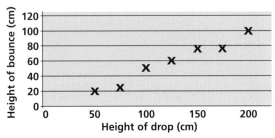

b) Comment on the relationship between the two sets of data.

The scatter diagram shows a strong positive correlation so you can draw the conclusion that the higher the drop the higher the bounce.

? Now try these...

1 a) Plot these points on a scatter diagram.

Height (cm)	127	165	149	147	155	161	154	138	145	167
Shoe size	5	8	5	6	5	5	6	4	5	7

b) Is there a correlation? If so, what does it tell us?

2 a) Draw a scatter diagram for the following data.

Distance travelled by a car (km)	50	100	150	200	250	300
Petrol left in tank (p)	55	52	49	43	40	38

b) Is there a correlation? If so, what does it tell us?

Example

The following table gives the golf scores of 14 people on two consecutive days

Mon	74	79	71	68	81	75	72	69	78	70	81	77	82	75
Tues	72	76	73	69	77	75	70	71	77	72	79	75	78	74

a) Plot this data on a scatter diagram and draw a line of best fit.

b) What does the graph show about the relationship between the two sets of data?
It shows a positive correlation.

c) Estimate the score of a person who scored 68 on Monday.
68.5

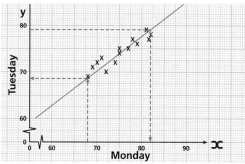
Draw a line up from 68 on the x-axis to the line of best fit, then across to the y-axis for your answer.

d) Estimate the score of a person who scored 79 on Tuesday.
82

You need to know...

• **how to draw a line of best fit on a scatter diagram.**

A perfect correlation between two sets of data produces points that lie on a straight line. However, not all scatter diagrams show a perfect correlation so a line of best fit is drawn instead. The line of best fit shows the approximate relationship or correlation between the two sets of data. A line of best fit should have the same number of points above and below it.

You can use the line of best fit to estimate one measurement if you are given the other. The more closely the points are clustered around the line of best fit, the better the estimate.

? Now try these...

1. An experiment was carried out with readings of values for x and y. Here are the results.

x	12	18	25	28	33	37	49	54	58	64
y	45	31	35	25	22	12	15	8	5	6

a) Plot these points on a scatter diagram and draw the line of best fit.
b) Comment on the relationship between the two sets of data.
c) Find an approximate value for y when x = 40.
d) Find an approximate value for x when y = 40.

✔ You should already know...

- **that the mode of a set of data is the value with the highest frequency**
- **that the median is the middle value**
- **that range is the difference between the biggest value and the smallest value.**

ℹ You need also to know...

- **how to find and use the mean of a set of discrete data**
- **how to use the range and one other average to compare two distributions.**

The **mean** is the numerical average. Averages such as a goal average in football matches or batting average in a cricket match are the mean. It is useful because it takes all values into account. To find the mean of a set of data simply add up all the values and then divide by the total number of values:

$$\text{Mean} = \frac{\text{all the values added together}}{\text{total number of values}}$$

When comparing two sets of data, remember that the mean is the value that best represents the set of data and the range shows the spread of the data – the larger the spread the less reliable the data.

? Now try these...

1. Find the mean and range of the following...
   a) 12, 14, 8, 14, 6, 12
   b) 49, 52, 57, 47, 51, 55, 52, 49, 53, 44
   c) £3.20, £3.70, £2.40, £3.50, £2.80
   d) 15°C, 16°C, 22°C, 21°C, 23°C, 17°C

2. These are the means and ranges for the times that it takes two taxi companies to get a taxi to a customer.

	Mean (min)	Range (min)
Super Cabs	9.7	14
Steve's Taxis	9.9	5

You have to leave to catch a train in 20 minutes. Which company would you call? Explain your answer.

Examples

1. The highest temperature (in °C) was recorded each day for a week: 18, 16, 21, 19, 23, 21, 22. Find the mean temperature.

$$\text{Mean} = \frac{18+16+21+19+23+21+22}{7} = 20°C$$

2. Use the data in the table below to find the mean number of sweets per tube.

> To find the mean of a large set of discrete data recorded in a frequency table, you need to add an extra column to the table.

No. of sweets in a tube	No. of tubes	No. of sweets in a tube x No. of tubes
34	12	34 x 12 = 408
35	24	35 x 24 = 840
36	31	36 x 31 = 1116
37	18	37 x 18 = 666
38	15	38 x 15 = 570
	Total = 100	Total = 3600

$$\text{Mean} = \frac{3600}{100} = 36$$

> This is the total number of sweets involved

3. Here are the runs scored by two cricketers in their last 6 innings. Which cricketer would you choose to play on your team? Explain your answer.

George	45	75	38	64	65	43
Ian	90	12	23	81	8	122

First calculate the means and ranges:

George: $\text{Mean} = \frac{330}{6} = 55$

           $\text{Range} = 75 - 38 = 37$

Ian: $\text{Mean} = \frac{336}{6} = 56$

           $\text{Range} = 122 - 8 = 114$

Ian has the largest mean but he also has the largest range. Choose George as he is more consistent – he is more likely to get his average number of runs. Ian has a chance of getting a high number of runs but this is risky because the large range shows he performs inconsistently.

Averages

You need to know...

- **how to find the modal class and estimate the mean, median and range of a set of grouped data**
- **how to select the most appropriate average**
- **how to compare two distributions using measures of average and range.**

The **modal class** is the class interval with the highest frequency.

The **median** is the exact middle value.

The **mean** for data collected in a group frequency table cannot be calculated exactly because the individual values are not known. However, it can be estimated by finding the midpoint value for each class interval (x) and using this as a representative value.

The formula for finding the mean of grouped data is:

$$\text{mean} = \frac{\sum fx}{\sum f}$$

where $\sum fx$ is the sum of all fx (frequency multiplied by mid-point) values.

The **range** is found by subtracting the lowest class boundary from the highest class boundary.

Example

The table shows the amount of rain (in millimetres) that fell on each day in April:

Amount of rain (mm)	Mid-point (x)	Frequency (f)	Mid point x frequency (fx)
0-5	2.5	9	2.5 x 9 = 22.5
5-10	7.5	8	7.5 x 8 = 60
10-15	12.5	7	12.5 x 7 = 87.5
15-20	17.5	4	17.5 x 4 = 70
20-25	22.5	2	22.5 x 2 = 45
	Totals	30	285

a) Complete the table and calculate an estimate for the mean.

> Add up all the numbers in the fx column and all the numbers in the frequency column and put the numbers in the formula.

$$\text{mean} = \frac{\sum fx}{\sum f}$$

$$= \frac{285}{30}$$

$$= 9.5$$

b) What is the modal group?

**The Modal group is 0 - 5.
(The class interval with the highest frequency.)**

c) What is the range?

**The range is 25 – 0 = 25
(The difference between the lowest class boundary and the highest class boundary)**

Now try these...

1 The table shows the results of a test:

Mark	Mid-point (x)	Number of pupils	Mid-point x frequency
30-39	34.5	3	
40-49	44.5	9	
50-59	54.5	10	
60-69	64.5	9	
70-79	74.5	12	
80-89	84.5	7	
	Totals		

a) Complete the table and calculate an estimate for the mean.

b) What is the modal group?

c) What is the range?

You also need to know...

- **how to construct cumulative frequency tables and diagrams.**

The **cumulative frequency** is a 'running total' and is found by adding each frequency to the sum of the previous ones. This gives the frequency up to a particular class boundary. To form a **cumulative frequency table** add two extra columns to the grouped frequency table. Write in the upper class boundaries and the running total.

The cumulative frequency table can be used to draw a **cumulative frequency diagram**. Plot the upper class boundary of each class interval on the x-axis and the corresponding cumulative frequency on the y-axis and then join the points with a smooth curve.

? Now try these...

1 A teacher asked 50 students in Year 9 how much time they had spent on their homework the previous night. The results are shown in the table.

Time in minutes	Frequency
$0<\text{time}\leqslant30$	6
$30<\text{time}\leqslant60$	14
$60<\text{time}\leqslant90$	21
$90<\text{time}\leqslant120$	9

a) Create and fill in a cumulative frequency table using the table above.
b) Draw the cumulative frequency curve.

Example

The table below shows the distribution of marks gained in an exam.

a) Complete the cumulative frequency column.

Marks	Frequency	Mark	Cumulative Frequency
0-10	1	$\leqslant 10$	1
11-20	2	$\leqslant 20$	3
21-30	13	$\leqslant 30$	16
31-40	24	$\leqslant 40$	40
41-50	32	$\leqslant 50$	72
51-60	16	$\leqslant 60$	88
61-70	11	$\leqslant 70$	99
71-80	1	$\leqslant 80$	100

b) Draw a cumulative frequency diagram.

All points are plotted at the upper class boundary of each class interval, so plot points at (0,0), (10,1), (20,3), etc.

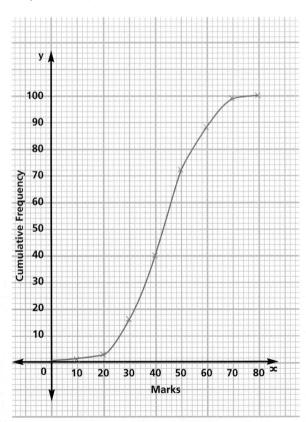

You need to know...

- **how to interpret cumulative frequency diagrams**
- **how to use the class boundaries to estimate the median and inter-quartile range**
- **how to use the median and inter-quartile range to compare distributions.**

Sets of data can be compared using the **median** and **inter-quartile range**.

The median is the middle value of the distribution.

To estimate the median...
1. find $\frac{1}{2}$ of the total frequency
2. draw a line across from this frequency on the y-axis until it hits the curve
3. draw a line down from this point to the x-axis
4. read off the estimate of the median.

To find the upper quartile...
1. find $\frac{3}{4}$ of the total frequency
2. draw a line across from this frequency on the y-axis until it hits the curve
3. draw a line down from this point to the x-axis
4. read off the value.

To find the lower quartile
1. find $\frac{1}{4}$ of the total frequency
2. draw a line across from this frequency on the y-axis until it hits the curve
3. draw a line down from this point to the x-axis
4. read off the value.

The inter-quartile range is found by subtracting the lower quartile value from the upper quartile value.

Example

Use the cumulative frequency diagram to find an estimate for...

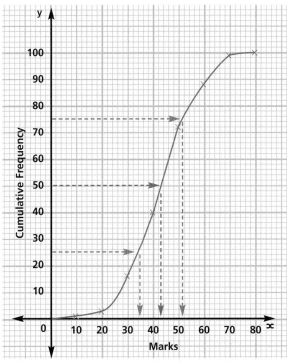

Marks

a) the median
$\frac{1}{2}$ x total cumulative frequency $= \frac{1}{2}$ x 100 = 50
Median = 43

b) the inter-quartile range.
Upper quartile =
$\frac{3}{4}$ x total cumulative frequency
$\frac{3}{4}$ x 100 = 75
Upper quartile = 52

> draw a line from 75 on the y-axis

Lower quartile =
$\frac{1}{4}$ x total cumulative frequency
$\frac{1}{4}$ x 100 = 25
Lower quartile = 35

> draw a line from 25 on the y-axis

Inter-quartile range = 52 – 35 = 17 marks

Now try these...

1. Use the cumulative frequency diagram you constructed for question 1 on page 118 to find...

    a) the median   **b)** the upper quartile
    c) the lower quartile   **d)** the inter-quartile range.

i You need to know...

- **how to understand and use the probability scale from 0 to 1**
- **how to justify probabilities using either experimental evidence or theoretical probability**
- **that different outcomes may result from repeating the same experiment.**

The probability of an event can be expressed numerically on the probability scale. All probabilities must be between 0 and 1.

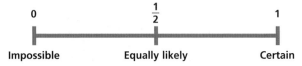

The more likely it is that an event will happen the closer the probability is to 1. The probability of an event happening is usually written as a fraction but it can be written as an equivalent decimal or a percentage (see p.25).

Theoretical probability is based around the idea that events are equally likely to happen if they have the same chance of happening, e.g. heads or tails.

For equally likely events the probability of an event is given using the formula:

$$P(event) = \frac{\text{Number of favourable outcomes}}{\text{Number of possible outcomes}}$$

In many real-life situations the probabilities are not equally likely and so you need to do a **survey** or an **experiment** to see which option is more likely, e.g. the probability of a car being red can be found by doing a traffic survey. If you repeat a survey it is unlikely that you will get exactly the same result, but the probability fractions should be about the same.

If events are not equally likely and you cannot do a survey or an experiment, then you can look at **statistical data** collected by others, e.g. to find the probability that it will snow on Christmas Day you can look at past records before estimating the probability.

Examples

1. A fair die is thrown. What is the probability of...

   a) throwing a six?
   Number of sixes on a die = 1.
   Total possible outcomes = 6
   (The six possible scores are 1, 2, 3, 4, 5, 6)
   P(scoring 6) = $\frac{1}{6}$

   b) throwing an even number?
   Number of even numbers = 3
   (The 3 possible even numbers are 2, 4, 6)
   P(even number) = $\frac{3}{6}$ = $\frac{1}{2}$

2. A bag contains 2 green counters, 7 red counters and 1 blue counter. Draw an arrow on the scale to represent each probability.

   A = Probability of selecting a red counter
   B = Probability of selecting a green counter
   C = Probability of selecting a blue counter

   $P(A) = \frac{7}{10}$ $P(B) = \frac{2}{10}$ $P(C) = \frac{1}{10}$

? Now try these...

1. 25 discs numbered from 1 to 25 are placed in a bag. One of these is chosen at random. What is the probability that the disc chosen is...
   a) a multiple of 3?
   b) greater than 15?
   c) a prime number?

2. Simon has 10 socks in his drawer, 3 of which are grey. He pulls out a sock at random. What is the probability that the sock Simon pulls out is grey?

3. The National Lottery uses 49 balls numbered 1 to 49. What is the probability that the first ball that comes out is a multiple of 10?

Probability

✓ You should already know...

- that if the chance of getting each outcome is the same, they are described as **equally likely**.

ℹ You also need to know...

- how to identify all possible outcomes for two or more events and present them in a table
- that the total of all the mutually exclusive events is 1 and use this to solve problems.

For a single event, e.g. rolling a die, you can list all the possible outcomes. For a **combined event**, e.g. rolling two dice and adding their scores, a **sample space diagram** can help to identify every possible result.

Mutually exclusive events are events which cannot happen at the same time. If you toss a coin the event 'obtain a head' and the event 'obtain a tail' are mutually exclusive.

The **total probability** for all possible outcomes is 1.

P(event will happen) = 1 – P(event will not happen)
P(event will not happen) = 1 – P(event will happen)

If you know the probability of an outcome you can use it to solve problems and make predictions (see Example 4).

? Now try these...

1. Draw a sample space diagram to show all possible outcomes when the score on the two spinners are added together.
   a) What is the total number of possible outcomes?
   b) Find the probability that the total is **i)** 11 **ii)** 5

2. There is a probability of $\frac{3}{10}$ that a caller will not leave a message on a telephone answer machine.
   a) What is P(caller leaves a message)?
   b) Out of 50 callers, how many would you expect to leave a message?

Examples

1. If you roll a red die and a blue die together how many different ways are there of scoring a total of 7?

   > List the outcomes methodically so you do not miss any.

   (1,6) (2,5) (3,4) (4,3) (5,2) (6,1)
   There are 6 ways of scoring 7.

2. Draw a sample space diagram to show the scores of two dice added together.

   First die

	1	2	3	4	5	6
1	2	3	4	5	6	7
2	3	4	5	6	7	8
3	4	5	6	7	8	9
4	5	6	7	8	9	10
5	6	7	8	9	10	11
6	7	8	9	10	11	12

   (Second die on vertical axis)

   a) What is the total number of possible outcomes?
      There are 36 possible outcomes.
   b) What is the probability of each outcome?
      $\frac{1}{36}$.
   c) Use the diagram to find out the probability of scoring a 7.
      P(scoring 7) = $\frac{6}{36}$ = $\frac{1}{6}$.

3. Out of every 100 people 17 are left-handed. What is the probability that a person chosen at random is...
   a) left-handed?
      P(Left-handed) = $\frac{17}{100}$
   b) right-handed?
      P(Right-handed) = P(Not left-handed)
      P(Not left-handed) = 1 – $\frac{17}{100}$ = $\frac{83}{100}$

4. The probability of passing the driving test at the first attempt is $\frac{2}{3}$. Of 60 people attempting the test for the first time how many would you expect to pass?
   Expected number = $\frac{2}{3}$ × 60 = 40

You need to know...

- **how to use relative frequency as an estimate of probability and how to use it to compare the outcomes of experiments.**

The relative frequency of an event can be used as an estimate of probability. If it is not possible to calculate probability, an experiment can be used to find the relative frequency. The frequency of an event is the number of times that event occurs in a number of trials.

$$\text{Relative frequency} = \frac{\text{Frequency of Event}}{\text{Total frequency}}$$

A bar chart can be drawn to compare the experimental frequency with the theoretical frequency. The more times an experiment is repeated, the closer to the theoretical frequency the relative frequency becomes.

Example

A die is thrown a number of times. The table shows the results.

Number on die	1	2	3	4	5	6
Frequency	14	19	21	22	20	24

a) Calculate the total frequency.
Total frequency
= 14 + 19 + 21 + 22 + 20 + 24 = 120

b) What is the frequency of scoring 4?
22

c) Calculate the relative frequency of scoring 4.
$$\frac{22}{120} = \frac{11}{60} \text{ or } 0.183$$

d) Work out the expected frequency of scoring 4 using theoretical probability.
$$P(4) = \frac{1}{6}$$
Expected number of fours $= \frac{1}{6} \times 120 = 20$

e) Draw a bar chart to compare the relative frequency and the expected frequency of each score.

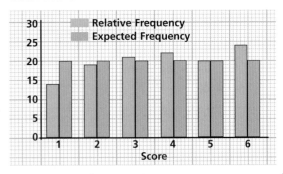

Now try these...

1 The table shows the number of advertisements on each page of a magazine.

Number of adverts	0	1	2	3	4	5	6
Frequency	18	35	24	14	7	0	2

a) Estimate the probability of a page chosen at random having more than 2 adverts.
b) If you completed a table for another magazine would you expect the estimate for **a)** to be the same? Explain your answer.

2 Two coins were tossed together 200 times. The results are shown in the table below:

2 heads	2 tails	1 head, 1 tail
49	43	108

Find the relative frequency of each event.

Examples

1 A bag contains 20 counters. 6 are black and 5 are white. A counter is selected at random. What is the probability that the counter is black or white?

P(Black) = $\frac{6}{20}$, P(White) = $\frac{5}{20}$

P(Black or White) = $\frac{6}{20}$ + $\frac{5}{20}$ = $\frac{11}{20}$

2 The probability that it will rain on any day in July is $\frac{1}{5}$. Find the probability that it will rain on the 2nd and 24th of July.

P(Raining on 2nd July) = $\frac{1}{5}$
P(Raining on 24th July) = $\frac{1}{5}$
P(Raining on 2nd and 24th July) = $\frac{1}{5} \times \frac{1}{5} = \frac{1}{25}$

3 The probability that Ajaz is late for school is 0.25. The probability that Hussain is late is 0.3. Assume that the boys do not know each other.

a) What is the probability that both boys are late for school?
P(Ajaz and Hussain are late)
= 0.25 x 0.3 = 0.075

b) Why do you need to assume they don't know each other?
The events have to be independent. If the boys knew each other they might walk in together so one being late might have an effect on the other being late.

ⓘ You need to know...

• **how and when to apply methods for calculating the probability of compound events.**

When dealing with the compound probability of two or more events always break them down into a sequence of single events. If two or more events are mutually exclusive (i.e. if one happens the other can't) the probability of A or B or C or D… happening is equal to the separate probabilities added together:

The OR rule
P(A or B) = P(A) + P(B)

If two or more events are independent (i.e. one event happening does not stop the other one from happening) the probability of A and B and C happening is found by multiplying the separate possibilities:

The AND rule
P(A and B) = P(A) x P(B)

❓ Now try these...

1 A box contains 20 counters. 1 is red, 5 are black, 10 are white and the rest are blue. 2 counters are drawn at random, the first being replaced before the second is chosen. Find the probability that…

a) the first counter drawn is blue.

b) the first counter is white and the second is blue.

c) one of the counters is white and the other red.

2 A biscuit jar contains 8 custard creams, 12 digestives, 15 chocolate digestives and 5 shortbread biscuits. If a biscuit is picked at random, what is the probability that it is…

a) a custard cream or a chocolate digestive?

b) not a custard cream?

Probability

i You also need to know...

- **how to use tree diagrams to display and calculate the outcomes of one or more events.**

When dealing with the probability of two or more events a tree diagram can be used to simplify the task. A tree diagram shows all the possible outcomes. By multiplying the probabilities along each branch, you can find the probability of each combined outcome.

The total probability always adds up to one. You can use this to check that your diagram is correct.

Example

The coach of a football team calculated the probabilities of each result for a home and an away game (see table alongside).

	Win	Lose	Draw
Home	0.6	0.3	0.1
Away	0.35	0.45	0.2

a) Draw a tree diagram to show all possible outcomes for a home game followed by an away game.

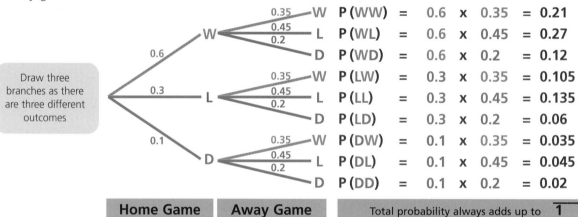

Draw three branches as there are three different outcomes

0.35	W	P (WW)	=	0.6	x	0.35	= 0.21
0.45	L	P (WL)	=	0.6	x	0.45	= 0.27
0.2	D	P (WD)	=	0.6	x	0.2	= 0.12
0.35	W	P (LW)	=	0.3	x	0.35	= 0.105
0.45	L	P (LL)	=	0.3	x	0.45	= 0.135
0.2	D	P (LD)	=	0.3	x	0.2	= 0.06
0.35	W	P (DW)	=	0.1	x	0.35	= 0.035
0.45	L	P (DL)	=	0.1	x	0.45	= 0.045
0.2	D	P (DD)	=	0.1	x	0.2	= 0.02

These are independent outcomes

Home Game   **Away Game**   Total probability always adds up to **1**

b) Calculate the probability that the team wins one game and loses one game.

P(wins 1 game, loses 1 game) = 0.27 + 0.105 = **0.375**

? Now try these...

1 At an old people's party, the probability that Ethel will win the Bingo prize is 0.15. The probability that she will win the raffle is 0.1.
   a) Draw a tree diagram to show all possible outcomes.
   b) Find the probability that Ethel wins only one of the two prizes.

2 When Ahmed and Katie play a game of table tennis the probability that Ahmed will win is $\frac{3}{8}$. When they play a game of snooker the probability that Katie will win is $\frac{3}{7}$.
   a) Draw a tree diagram to show all possible outcomes.
   b) Calculate the probability that Katie will win only one game.

Notes

Index